A CITY'S WORTH OF ANGRY FACES STARING AT ME LIKE I AM—WHICH, I PROMISE YOU, **I'M NOT.**

N.O. TO

00:21

N.O. N.O. SAY NO TO ART!

THE STADIUM IS FILLED TO CAPACITY— PAST CAPACITY...

...BUT THERE ARE NO FOOTBALL TEAMS HERE TODAY.

THIS TOTAL ABOMINATION IS BEING BROADCAST ON TV AND THE INTERNET TOO.
ALL THE USELESS MAGAZINES ARE HERE, ALL THE NEWSPAPERS.
00:20
N.O.
N.O.
N.O.
THEY DON'T CARE. THERE ARE NO TEARS. NO WORDS OF PROTEST. NO FISTS RAISED IN SOLIDARITY.

N.O.
N.O.
N.O.
N.O.
N.O.
N.O.
N.O.
NOT A GOOD DAY FOR US ALLGOODS. IN FACT...
...IT'S LOOKING LIKE IT WILL BE OUR LAST.

HE IS THE REASON.
I KNOW WHO HE IS. I'VE ACTUALLY MET HIM.
N.O.
N.O.
N.O.

HIS ONENESS. THE HEAD OF THE NEW ORDER.
THE ONE WHO IS THE ONE!
THE ONE WHO IS THE ONE!
THE ONE WHO IS THE ONE!
N.O.
N.O.
N.O.

SHOVE
GHK!

THERE IS MY BROTHER, WHIT, HANDSOME AND BRAVE.
MY FATHER, BEATEN, BUT STILL TRYING TO CHEER US UP WITH A SMILE.
MY MOTHER, CRYING, NOT FOR HERSELF, BUT FOR ME AND WHIT.
BUT I'M GETTING AHEAD OF MYSELF.

BY ORDER OF THE NEW ORDER,

and the Great Wind—The One Who Is

THE ONE—

let it be known that as of

NOW, THIS MOMENT, or

TWELVE O'CLOCK MIDNIGHT,

whichever shall arrive first, following the **SWIFT TRIUMPH** of the **ORDER** of the **ONES WHO PROTECT**, who have obliterated the **BLIND AND DUMB FORCES** of passivity and complacency **PLAGUING** this world, **ALL CITIZENS** *must, shall,* and *will* abide by

THESE THREE ORDERS FOR ORDER:

1. All behaviors NOT in keeping with N.O. law, logic, order, and science (including but not limited to theology, philosophy, and IN PARTICULAR the creative and dark arts, et cetera) are hereby ABOLISHED.
2. ALL persons under eighteen years of age will be evaluated for ORDERLINESS and MUST COMPLY with the prescribed corrective actions.
3. The One Who Is THE ONE grants, appoints, decides, seizes, and executes at will. All NOT complying shall be SEIZED and/or EXECUTED.

—As declared to The One Who Writes Decrees
by THE ONE WHO IS THE ONE

Z

...News time... ...from today...
......
......

TURN
...CELIA...
DRUB. DRUB.

?
DRUB
DRUB
DRUB

DRUB
DRUB
DRUB
SSKT

DRUB
DRUB
DRUB

CRASH
!!
HANDS BEHIND YOUR HEAD!!
WHAT ARE YOU DOING IN OUR HOUSE??

CRASH
CRASH
STUMBLE
THUD
...?
AW, WHIT... BULL IN A CHINA SHOP...
CRASH
!!

IT'S HER! WISTERIA ALLGOOD!
WHO ARE YOU?! WHAT ARE YOU DOING IN MY FREAKING BEDROOM?
WE'RE FROM THE NEW ORDER. YOU'RE COMING WITH US.
UM, I-I...
I NEED TO PUT ON SOME CLOTHES. C-CAN I HAVE SOME PRIVACY?
SHUT UP!
YOU TWO, GRAB HER AND BE CAREFUL! SHE'S DANGEROUS—THEY ALL ARE.
NO! STOP! DON'T YOU DARE!! MOM, DAD!!!

THUD
WISTY, ARE YOU OKAY??
ACK!
WHIT, WHAT'S GOING ON? WHO ARE THESE... MONSTERS?
N.O.
N.O.
WHERE'RE MOM AND DAD?
THWACK

...MOM!!
DAD!!
WISTY!!
YOU AND WHIT ARE SPECIAL, HONEY. REALLY SPECIAL.

ALL PARENTS THINK THEIR KIDS ARE SPECIAL.
SOMETIMES PEOPLE ARE AFRAID OF THOSE WHO ARE DIFFERENT.
I MEAN, YOU'RE REALLY SPECIAL, WISTY. PAY ATTENTION, DEAR.
BEING AFRAID MAKES THEM ANGRY AND UNREASONABLE.
WISTERIA ALLGOOD?
?!
BYRON SWAIN?

WHAT ARE *YOU* DOING HERE, SWAIN? GET OUT OF MY HOUSE!

MAKE ME.

RST

WISTERIA ALLGOOD, THE NEW ORDER IS TAKING YOU INTO CUSTODY UNTIL YOUR TRIAL.

YOU ARE HEREBY ACCUSED OF BEING A WITCH.

...!

A WITCH? ARE YOU NUTS?? DID WE JUST GO BACK IN TIME?! LAST I LOOKED THIS WAS THE TWENTY-FIRST CENTURY, NOT THE SEVENTEENTH!

WHITFORD ALLGOOD...

THERE'S NO SUCH THING AS WITCHES OR WIZARDS! FAIRY TALES ARE A LOAD OF CRAP. WHO DO YOU THINK YOU ARE, YOU CREEPY LITTLE WEASEL?!
...

ACCORDING TO THE NEW ORDER CODE, YOU MAY EACH TAKE ONE POSSESSION FROM THE HOUSE.
I DON'T APPROVE, BUT THAT'S THE LETTER OF THE LAW AND I WILL ABIDE BY IT, OF COURSE.
...!

NOD

GRAB
KTK
N.O.
N.O.

...HUH?
PLEASE, JUST TAKE IT, WISTERIA. TAKE THE DRUMSTICK.
I LOVE YOU SO MUCH, SWEETHEART.
I LOVE YOU, WHIT.
SNATCH!
FLIP FLIP
IT'S BLANK!
YEAH, LIKE YOUR SOCIAL CALENDAR.
SLAM

THWACK
SMOOTH
DON'T YOU DARE—!!
TAKE THEM TO THE VAN.
NO!
YOU DON'T HAVE THE RIGHT!!
MOM!! DAD!!

LET.
ME.
GO!!

....?!
...HUH??
WHAT DID YOU DO TO HER?!
SHOVE
WISTY!!!

HUH
HUH
COUGH
COUGH
SPLASH
SEE?! SEE?! SEE?! LOCK HER UP! SHOOT HER IF YOU HAVE TO. WHATEVER IT TAKES!
COUGH
SHIVER
...!
!?
WOOSH
YOU...!

CRAS
SHAA

HELLO, ALLGOOD FAMILY.
I AM THE ONE WHO IS THE ONE. PERHAPS YOU'VE HEARD OF ME?
WE KNOW WHO YOU ARE. WE'RE NOT AFRAID OF YOU, THOUGH, AND WE WON'T BEND TO YOUR UGLY RULES.
I WOULDN'T EXPECT YOU TO BEND TO ANY RULES, BENJAMIN.
OR YOU, ELIZA. ASPIRING DEVIANTS LIKE YOU ALWAYS VALUE FREEDOM ABOVE ALL ELSE. BUT IT DOESN'T MATTER WHETHER YOU ACCEPT THIS NEW REALITY OR NOT.
IT'S THE YOUNGINS I'M HERE TO SEE.
THIS IS A COMMAND PERFORMANCE, YOU UNDERSTAND. I COMMAND, THEY OBEY.

I WILL MAKE IT SIMPLE FOR THE TWO OF YOU. ALL YOU HAVE TO DO IS RENOUNCE YOUR FORMER EXISTENCE—YOUR FREEDOMS, YOUR WAY OF LIFE, AND YOUR PARENTS IN PARTICULAR—AND YOU WILL BE SPARED. NOT A HAIR ON YOUR HEADS WILL BE TOUCHED. I PROMISE.
THAT'S ALL. SIMPLE AS APPLE PIE.
NO WAY!
NOT GOING TO HAPPEN. EVER! WE RENOUNCE YOU, YOUR BALDNESS, YOUR TERRIBLE-NESS!
CHUCKLE
WHITFORD ALLGOOD.
FREEZE
PERFECT GRADES, THE FASTEST QUARTER-BACK ON THE TEAM, THE HEARTTHROB OF EVERY GIRL IN SCHOOL. I KNOW YOU WERE A VERY GOOD BOY UNTIL RECENTLY, EVER SINCE THE SAD AND UNFORTUNATE DISAPPEARANCE...
...OF YOUR GIRLFRIEND AND SOUL MATE, CELIA.

THE QUESTION IS, CAN YOU BE GOOD AGAIN?
CAN YOU LEARN TO OBEY THE RULES?
...
HMM.
WISTERIA ALLGOOD, I KNOW ALL ABOUT YOU TOO.
DISOBEDIENT, RECALCITRANT, A TRUANT, OVER TWO WEEKS OF DETENTION DUE TO BE SERVED AT YOUR HIGH SCHOOL.
THE QUESTION IS, CAN YOU EVER BE GOOD? CAN YOU POSSIBLY LEARN TO OBEY?
CURTSY
OF COURSE, SIR, YOUR EVERY WAKING WISH IS MY COMMA—
ENOUGH.

TAKE THEM AWAY!
THEY SHALL NEVER SEE THEIR PARENTS AGAIN.
NOR SHALL YOU, BEN AND ELIZA, SEE YOUR VERY SPECIAL OFF-SPRING...
...UNTIL THE DAY YOU ALL DIE.

N.O. REFORMATORY
THUNK
OKAY, NOW WATCH 'EM CLOSELY. YOU KNOW, THEY'RE—
YEAH, WE KNOW. I GOT THE BURNS TO PROVE IT.
DON'T YOU GUYS FEEL KIND OF DUMB?
I MEAN, A DOZEN GIANT MEN, JUST FOR US TWO KIDS— IT'S KIND OF EMBARRASS—
BE QUIET!

SNAP
0346701
SNAP
0346702
PUSH
SHOVE
OW...
WISTY, YOU OKAY?
SORT OF. IF I'M ALLOWED TO TOTALLY CHANGE WHAT "OKAY" MEANS.
WE'LL GET OUT OF HERE. THIS IS ALL JUST A STUPID MISTAKE.
AU CONTRAIRE, MY NAIVE AMIGO.

WHAT? WHO ARE YOU?

I'M PRISONER NUMBER 450209A. TRUST ME, THERE'S BEEN NO MISTAKE. AND THEY DIDN'T FORGET TO READ YOU YOUR RIGHTS.

AND THEY AREN'T GOING TO GIVE YOU A LAWYER OR A PHONE CALL. AND YOUR MAMA AND PAPA AREN'T COMING TO GET YOU. EVER. AND THAT'S A LONG, LONG TIME.

WHAT DO YOU KNOW ABOUT IT?

LOOK, HOW OLD ARE YOU?

I'M ALMOST EIGHTEEN AND MY SISTER'S FIFTEEN.

WELL, I'M THIRTEEN. SO YOU'LL FIT RIGHT IN HERE.

YUP, IT'S PRETTY MUCH JUST US KIDS AROUND HERE THESE DAYS.

...DO YOU HAVE ANY IDEA WHAT'S GOING ON?
NOT A WHOLE LOT, JEFE. BUT I HEARD SOME OF THE GUARDS TALKING ABOUT A CLEAN SWEEP. YOU REMEMBER HEARING ABOUT THE NEW ORDER?
YEAH, BUT I WASN'T REALLY PAYING ATTENTION.
...
OKAY, SO YOU'VE BEEN LIVING INSIDE YOUR HEAD. BUT, IF IT'S ANY CONSOLATION, SO WAS MOST OF THE REST OF THE COUNTRY.
SEE, THE NEW ORDER IS THE POLITICAL PARTY THAT'S BEEN WINNING ALL THE ELECTIONS.
PUSH
THEY'RE IN CHARGE NOW. IN JUST A FEW MONTHS THEY'VE GUTTED THE OLD GOVERNMENT AND INSTITUTED THE COUNCIL OF ONES.

HEARD OF THEM? THE ONE IN COMMAND, THE ONE WHO JUDGES, THE ONE WHO IMPRISONS, THE ONE WHO IS THE ONE, BLAH, BLAH.
OKAY, SO, THE NEW ORDER. POLITICS. WHAT'S THAT GOT TO DO WITH US?
THEY'RE THE LAW *AND* THEY'RE THE ORDER, AMIGOS.
BUT WHY ARE THEY DOING THESE UNSPEAKABLE THINGS TO *KIDS*?
BECAUSE WE TALK BACK? BECAUSE WE'RE HARD TO CONTROL? BECAUSE WE HAVE AN *IMAGINATION*? WHO KNOWS? WHY DON'T YOU ASK THE ONE WHO JUDGES...
...AT YOUR TRIAL.
TRIAL? WHAT TRIAL? WE'RE GOING TO TRIAL? FOR WHAT?
WHAM
OW!
IF YOU KEEP TALKING TO THE OTHER PRISONERS, I'LL PUT YOU ALL IN SOLITARY!

FOOM
ARGH!!
AAAAAAAAA!!!
!
WHIT, DID YOU SEE—
WISTY!! DUCK!
PFRLT

SHOVE

TOSS

MISS ME?

WITCH & WIZARD

BET YOU THOUGHT YOU WERE SO TOUGH AT SCHOOL, RACKING UP DETENTION, HUH?
LET'S SEE HOW TOUGH YOU ARE *NOW*.
HEY WHIT, LOOK! IT'S THE PET FERRET WITH HALL-MONITOR ASPIRATIONS. *AGAIN*.
IT'S A *TRAINED* PET FERRET TOO. I THINK IT JUST TALKED.
...WHA...?!

HAVE YOU BEEN WORKING OUT, SWAIN? I MEAN, IT DOESN'T LOOK IT, BUT DON'T YOU NEED AT LEAST SIX GUARDS BACKING YOU UP?
LET'S CUT THE CHIT-CHAT.
WE BOTH KNOW WHY YOU'RE HERE, HMM?
THE SOONER YOU ADMIT YOUR SECRETS AND TELL US WHAT WE WANT TO KNOW, THE BETTER IT WILL BE FOR YOU AND YOUR FREAKY FIRE-BREATHING SISTER.
GOT NO IDEA WHAT YOU'RE TALKING ABOUT, SKIPPY.
YOU CAN BACK OFF THE DRAMA-QUEEN PERFORMANCE, OKAY?
ARE YOU TWO MISCREANTS PROTECTING SOMEONE?!

WELL, THEY'RE CERTAINLY NOT PROTECTING YOU. YOUR GOOD "FRIENDS" HAVE ALREADY TOLD US EVERYTHING WE NEED TO KNOW. IT WAS BEAUTIFUL. I MEAN, A HANDFUL OF MARBLES COULDN'T HAVE ROLLED ANY EASIER.
THAT RIGHT? WHAT TERRIBLE SECRETS DID THEY TELL YOU? MY GAMING CHEAT CODES? THE "D" ON MY LAST BIO TEST THAT MY FOLKS DON'T KNOW ABOUT? SOMEHOW, GETTING GROUNDED ISN'T THE THREAT IT USED TO BE!
YOU ALMOST FLUNKED BIOLOGY? COOL.
YEAH.
...
SHUT UP, FREAK! I SAW WHAT YOU DID EARLIER! YOU BURST INTO FLAMES! AND YOU WEREN'T EVEN HURT AFTERWARD! IF THAT'S NOT SICK AND WRONG, I DON'T KNOW WHAT IS!
YOU KNOW, BYRON, *YOU'RE* THE FREAK, ACTUALLY. WE COULD PUT *YOU* ON OUR SECRET VOODOO WITCHCRAFTY TO-DO LIST.

GRAB
YOU!!
AAA!!
KRKL

. . .
MORE PROOF!!!
YOU ARE A WITCH!! YOU'LL BE LOCKED UP FOREVER!
??
SLAM
DON'T EVEN THINK ABOUT TRYING ANYTHING. YOUR TRIAL IS TOMORROW.
JINGLE

...
WHIT, ARE YOU THERE?
I'M HERE, SIS.
HOW CAN THIS BE HAPPENING?
THIS FEELS LIKE A NIGHT-MARE, ONLY I CAN'T WAKE UP.
...

Z
Z

HI, WHIT, MISSED YOU.

!!
CELIA?
I'M TRYING TO ACT CASUAL, AND FAILING PRETTY BAD. SORRY.
ARE YOU OKAY? WHAT HAPPENED TO YOU?

WE'LL GET TO ALL THAT. I PROMISE. THE QUESTION IS, ARE YOU OKAY? IS WISTY?
SURE—YOU KNOW ME, CELIA, I CAN ROLL WITH IT. AND WISTY'S TOUGH AS NAILS. I GUESS WE'RE A LITTLE WEIRDED OUT, THOUGH.
YOU LOOK GREAT, WHIT—FOR SOMEBODY WHO'S BEEN KIDNAPPED, BEATEN UP, AND JAILED ILLEGALLY.
FORGET ABOUT ME. I WANT TO HEAR EVERY-THING ABOUT YOU. CELIA, *WHAT* IS GOING ON? WHERE DID YOU GO?
THAT'S A TOUGH QUESTION.
AND I KNOW I JUST GOT HERE, WHIT, BUT I REALLY HAVE TO GO NOW. AND WHIT—
...!
IT'S HARD TO BELIEVE *I'M* SAYING THIS TO *YOU*, OF ALL PEOPLE—YOU REALLY HAVE TO HANG TOUGH. YOU AND WISTERIA.

CELIA...
OTHERWISE YOU'LL BOTH BE DEAD.
...
CLANG!
WAKE UP, YOU RATS!
IT'S YOUR DAY IN COURT, WITCH AND WIZARD. NOW YOU GET TO MEET THE ONE WHO JUDGES!
CLINK
CLANG

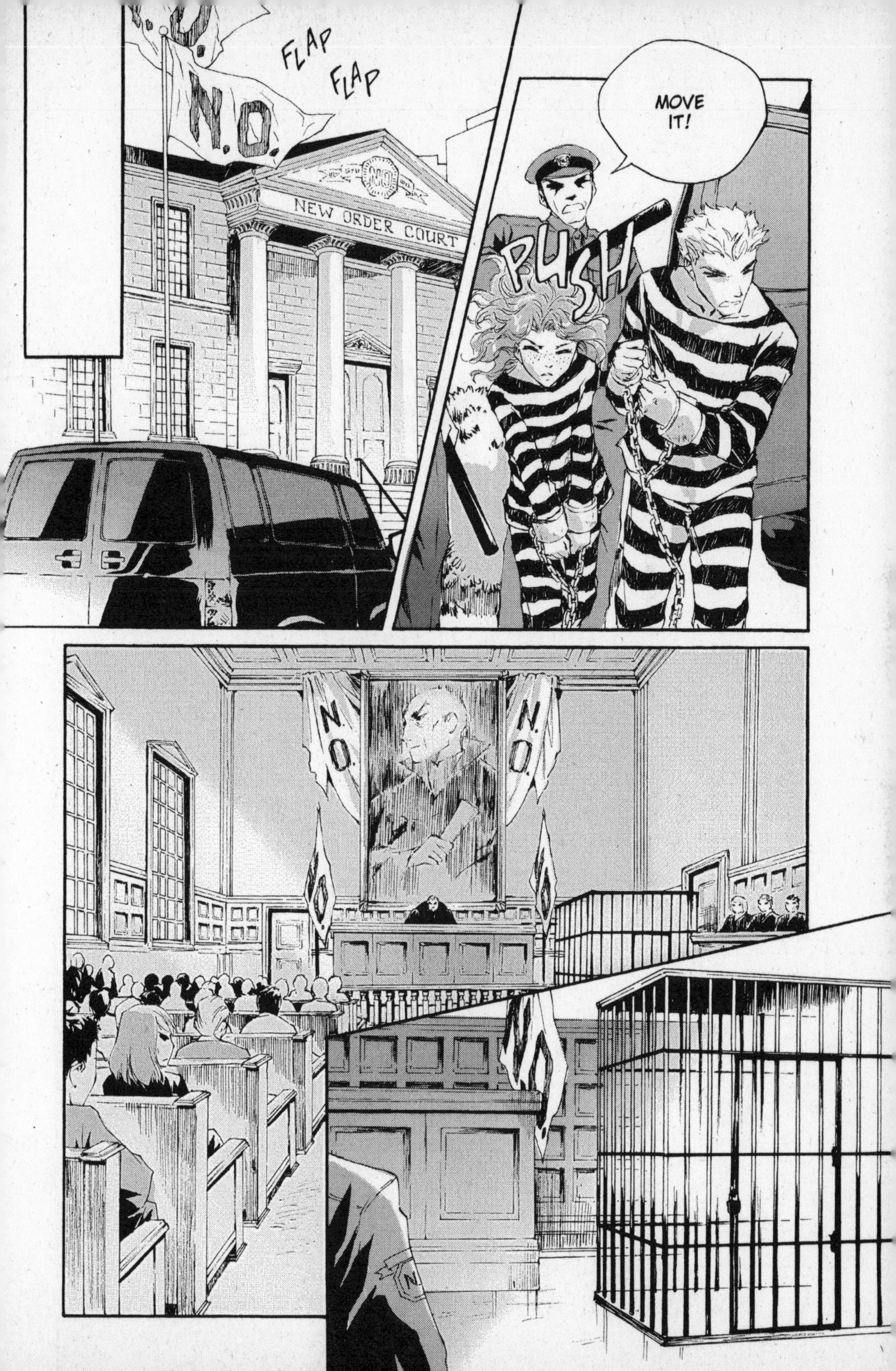

N.O.
FLAP
FLAP
NEW ORDER COURT
MOVE IT!
PUSH
N.O.
N.O.

SHOVE
I'M ALMOST GETTING USED TO LOOKING THROUGH BARS.
DON'T SAY THAT. WE'RE GETTING OUT OF THIS MADHOUSE. I PROMISE.
...
WHITFORD ALLGOOD! WISTERIA ALLGOOD!
THIS TRIAL IS CONVENED BECAUSE YOU ARE ACCUSED OF THE MOST SERIOUS CRIMES AGAINST THE NEW ORDER!

WHAT HAVE WE DONE? JUST TELL US THAT. WHAT ARE WE ACCUSED OF?
SILENCE!!
LISTEN, YOU CONTEMPTUOUS GIRL! YOU ARE A MOST DANGEROUS THREAT TO EVERYTHING THAT IS PROPER AND RIGHT AND GOOD. WE KNOW THIS FROM INNUMERABLE INVESTIGATIONS UNDERTAKEN BY THE NEW ORDER'S INVESTIGATIVE SECURITY AGENCY...
NOD
NOD
...AND WE KNOW THIS, MOST FUNDAMENTALLY...
NOD
...BECAUSE OF THE PROPHECY.
HOW SAY YOU TO THESE CHARGES?

NOT GUILTY!!
GENTLEMEN OF THE JURY, WITH THAT STATEMENT, THE DEFENDANTS STAND IN CLEAR CONTEMPT OF YOUR WILL AND THIS COURT'S MISSION. THEY MOCK US. THEY FLOUT THE STANDARDS OF THE GLORIOUS NEW ORDER!
I ASK YOU, WHAT IS YOUR VERDICT?
!?
RAISE
RAISE
...THAT'S IT?? THAT'S OUR TRIAL??
SILENCE!
DON'T WE GET A LAWYER?? THIS IS NOT FAIR!!
WHAM

TURN
TURN
TURN
GUILTY AS CHARGED!
BAM
BAM
YOU, WISTERIA ALLGOOD, ARE HEREBY DETERMINED BY THE NEW ORDER TO BE A WITCH! YOU, WHITFORD ALLGOOD, ARE DETERMINED TO BE A WIZARD!
BOTH OF WHICH ARE PUNISHABLE BY HANGING...
...UNTIL DEAD.

!!
HANG IN THERE, WISTY.
THIS...THIS ISN'T REAL.
...UNFORTUNATELY, EXECUTIONS ARE NOT ALLOWED UNTIL SAID CRIMINAL IS EIGHTEEN YEARS OF AGE. THEREFORE, BOTH OF YOU WILL BE HELD IN THE STATE PENITENTIARY FOR THE TIME BEING.
NOW, TAKE THEM OUT OF MY SIGHT.
YOU'RE MAKING A TERRIBLE MISTAKE!! THIS IS INSANE! YOU'LL BE DISBARRED! THIS ISN'T LEGAL!
DRAG
DRAG

SHUT UP, WIZARD!!
HURL
FREEZE
SMACK

WIZARD!!
WITCH!
EXECUTE THEM BOTH!!
PUT THEM TO DEATH!
YOU DON'T HAVE THE RIGHT!! WHERE IS OUR LAWYER?!

WANTED
DEAD OR ALIVE

....!
WISTY, LOOK!!
TWIST

GET IN!
TOSS

SLAM
DID YOU SEE THE POSTER? IT WAS MOM AND DAD!
THEY GOT AWAY. THEY'RE OUT THERE SOMEWHERE.
SOMEHOW, WE'LL FIND THEM!
N.O.
N.O.
N.O.
SAY N.O. TO MAGIC
WANTED
NEW ORDER COURT
NOT
LK ON
RASS
EXIT ONLY

WITCH & WIZARD

KRRK
GENERAL BOWEN STATE PSYCHIATRIC HOSPITAL
SPLASH

!!
...WHY ARE YOU SO HAPPY? THIS LOOKS LIKE A HELL-HOUSE.
NO, NO, THIS IS A PSYCHIATRIC HOSPITAL! THIS EXPLAINS SO MUCH!
...I'M CRAZY!! EVERYTHING HAS BEEN MY DELUSIONS!
WILL I BE TREATED HERE? WHEN CAN I MEET WITH THE DOCTOR?

SMACK
THIS IS A JAIL OF THE NEW ORDER, GIRLIE. KEEP MOVING.

DER
strator
YES?
WHY ARE YOU BOTHERING ME?
TWO MORE DESPICABLE DEGENERATES FOR YOU, MATRON. A WITCH AND A WIZARD.
RISE
POLICE MUST BE DREDGING EVERY RANCID TRASH PILE IN THE COUNTRY FINDING ALL THIS...FILTH FOR ME TO LOOK AFTER.
DON'T KNOW WHAT THEY EXPECT ME TO DO WITH ALL THESE MAGGOTS.
"MAGGOTS" IS RIGHT, MA'AM, THOUGH TOO KIND, IF YOU ASK ME!
I DIDN'T!
!!

PUSH
TOSS
WELCOME TO DEATH ROW, VERMIN.
SLAM
KCHK CLICK
O-OKAY, THIS PLACE IS A LITTLE CREEPY, HUH?
UH, NOT AS CREEPY AS YOU, SIS. DO YOU KNOW YOU'RE
HUH??!
HAVE YOU BEEN PLAYING IN TOXIC WASTE LATELY? DO ME A FAVOR AND HIT THE DIMMER SWITCH.

WHAT'S WRONG WITH ME?!
I-I DON'T KNOW HOW!
BRUSH BRUSH
MOM...MOM AND DAD ALWAYS TOLD ME ABOUT EVERYTHING.
WHY DIDN'T THEY TELL ME ANY OF THIS...?
...

WHIT...

TAP TAP
CREAK
WATCH YOURSELF, NOW. THESE ARE DANGEROUS FIENDS.
THANK YOU FOR YOUR CONCERN, MATRON, BUT I THINK I'LL BE JUST FINE.
...?
...AND WHO ARE YOU SUPPOSED TO B—
SMACK
AH!

YOUR EVIL POWERS WILL NOT WORK, WITCH.
I AM YOUR *VISITOR*. I WILL BE HERE TO MAKE SURE YOU BEHAVE AND WILL METE OUT THE PUNISHMENT WHEN YOU DON'T.
LEAVE HER ALONE, YOU COWARDLY FREA—
SMACK
THIS IS YOUR FIRST DAY AT THE HOSPITAL, WIZARD, SO I'LL BE GENTLE. BUT YOU WON'T EVER SPEAK TO THE MATRON OR ME THAT WAY AGAIN...
...OR THINGS WILL GET WORSE.
WORSE? YOU MEAN WORSE THAN BEING KIDNAPPED DURING THE NIGHT, SENTENCED TO DEATH IN A LAUGHABLE TRIAL, AND THEN LOCKED UP IN A CONDEMNED HOSPITAL WITH TWO SADISTS? IT'S GOING TO GET WORSE?!

SMACK
SMACK
SMACK
YESSSS. MUCH WORSE. YOUR FILE INDICATED YOU WEREN'T THE BRIGHTEST BULB IN THE CHANDELIER, BUT EVEN YOU SHOULD BE ABLE TO GRASP THIS MUCH...
THIS IS YOUR NEW HOME.
SHUH
SHUH
YOU ALSO HAVE YOUR OWN SEMIPRIVATE BATHROOM, COMPLETE WITH OUR SPECIAL-ISSUE TOILET PAPER, THAT FEELS SO AIRY...
PLEASE NOTE THAT YOU HAVE ONE EXTERNAL WINDOW.
BEYOND IT IS THE TEN-STORY-DEEP VENTILATION SHAFT, THE BOTTOM OF WHICH IS FITTED WITH A TURBINE THAT COULD GRIND A BLUE WHALE INTO MUSH IN LESS THAN TEN SECONDS. FEEL FREE TO THROW YOURSELVES DOWN IT AT ANY TIME.

...YOU'LL SWEAR IT'S NOT EVEN THERE.

IT REALLY ISN'T.

WE HAVE ARMED GUARDS, SECURITY CAMERAS, ELECTRONIC PERIMETERS, AND MULTIPLE LETHAL SAFEGUARDS THAT I'M NOT AT LIBERTY TO DISCUSS.

WTH

ALSO, YOUR EVIL TRICKERY WILL NOT WORK HERE, AS THIS ENTIRE BUILDING HAS BEEN ALTERED TO DAMPEN YOUR ENERGIES. IN SHORT, ONCE YOU WALKED IN THE DOOR...

...YOU EFFECTIVELY BECAME NORMAL.

YOU WILL LEARN TO BE SILENT WHILE I SPEAK.
AND TO HELP YOU EMBRACE THE CONCEPT, YOUR PUNISHMENT WILL BE TO CLEAN THIS BATHROOM UNTIL SPOTLESS.
WITH *THIS.*
ARE YOU KIDDING M—
TWICE.
UNTIL IT'S OPERATING-ROOM HYGIENIC.
TAP TAP
AND NOW, EVEN THOUGH IT'S A WASTE OF TAXPAYERS' MONEY...
...I SUPPOSE YOU SHOULD LEARN HOW TO GET YOUR FOOD.
COME WITH ME, VERMIN.

SNARL
BARK
BARK
SNRL
...WHAT IS THIS? NOW WHAT?
...ARE THESE DOGS? OR WOLVES?
I'M GOING WITH HELL-HOUNDS.
THERE'S FOOD WAY, WAY, WAY DOWN THERE. AND WATER. USE YOUR PAILS. YOU HAVE FOUR MINUTES, AND IF YOU'RE NOT BACK BY THEN...I'LL KNOW YOU'VE PASSED TO THE OTHER SIDE. VIOLENTLY.
SNRL
SNAP
UH. DO YOU THINK MAYBE YOU COULD BURST INTO FLAMES AGAIN?
I CAN'T DO IT ON PURPOSE. I'M TRYING. NOT HAPPENING.

CLATTER
OKAY, I'LL GO. I'M SUPPOSED TO BE THE FASTEST QUARTERBACK, RIGHT?
SNARL
SNAP
SNAP

I... I DID IT.
HUH HUH
FOUL!
CLATTER
CHOMP
...!
FOUR MINUTES AND SIX SECONDS! NO FOOD! NO WATER!
KEEP YOUR HANDS OFF—

BZZT
FUMP
TWITCH
TWITCH
BZT
YOU STILL DON'T GET IT, WIZARD. LEARN FASTER, OR YOU WON'T SURVIVE THE TESTS.
...TESTS?

FOUL!!

...HOW LONG HAVE WE BEEN IN HERE?
NO IDEA. DAYS? WEEKS? SOME OF THE OLD BRUISES ARE STARTING TO HEAL.
THIS LOOKS OPERATING-ROOM HYGIENIC, DOESN'T IT?
STILL NOT SILENT WHEN VISITOR SPEAKS, OOPS.
IT'S THE THIRTIETH TIME HE'S MAKING YOU SCRUB THAT. COULD PROBABLY EAT THERE NOW.
EW.
ARGH, WE HAVE TO GET OUT OF HERE!! WE HAVE SOME SORT OF POWERS! SHOULDN'T WE BE ABLE TO USE THEM??
YEAH, AND THEY'RE GROWING TOO. I'M APPARENTLY IMMUNE TO THEIR STUNGUNS AS OF TODAY...ANY WEIRD-O MAGIC HAPPENINGS FROM YOU?
I FLOATED IN MY SLEEP AGAIN LAST NIGHT.

AND I'VE BEEN TRYING TO MAKE UP SOME SPELLS... BUT NOTHING'S WORKED SO FAR.

MOM AND DAD SHOULD'VE GIVEN US SOMETHING THAT'S ACTUALLY HELPFUL.

OPEN

NOT JUST A STUPID DRUMSTICK AND A MUSTY OLD...

...BLANK BOOK?

HUH

FLIP FLIP

!!

OH WOOOW! *HISTORY OF WORLD ART??* THE SCHOOL LIBRARY NEVER EVER HAD THIS ONE OUT...
...WAIT, WHAT?
NO, NO, IT'S THE NEXT BOOK IN THE PERCIVAL JOHNSON SERIES, SEE?
...WAIT, NO.

NOW IT'S *THE SWIM-SUIT ISSUE DELUXE.*
HUH? ARE WE LOOKING AT THE SAME BOOK?? I SEE THE NEW NOVEL BY K.J. MEYERS!!
...

WHIT, I THINK...IT'S SHOWING EACH OF US WHAT WE WANT TO SEE. IT'S MAGIC.
THAT'S WHY DAD GAVE IT TO YOU.
...

SHOW ME WHERE CELIA IS.

...

UH.
...COOL.
WHIT, COME BACK HERE THIS SECOND!! WHITFORD!!
BLINK BLINK
...WOW.

WITCH & WIZARD

SQ UINT
TURN
!
!
IS SOME-ONE THERE?
CELIA...!
IT'S ME, WHIT! I'M HERE. CAN YOU SEE ME?

WHIT? I CAN SEE YOU. HOW DID YOU—WHERE ARE YOU?
...
BELIEVE IT OR NOT, I'M IN THE BATHROOM OF A CELL IN A MENTAL HOSPITAL. BUT WHERE ARE YOU?
WHIT, YOU HAVE TO GO RIGHT NOW. YOU SHOULDN'T BE HERE. IT'S DANGEROUS!
WHY?!
I'M SORRY, BUT I HAVE TO TELL YOU WHAT REALLY HAPPENED TO ME.
THEY MURDERED ME. THEY SAID...IT WAS BECAUSE OF YOU AND YOUR SISTER. IT HAPPENED AT THE HOSPITAL... THE ONE WHO IS THE ONE—HE'S SO AWFUL, SO POWERFUL.
...
...I SEE YOU. YOU SAID WE'D MEET. AND YOU'RE HERE WITH ME.
YOU'RE NOT DEAD.
DON'T COME HERE AGAIN, WHIT. THIS IS THE SHADOW-LAND. IT'S A PLACE FOR SPIRITS.

THAT'S WHAT I AM NOW. I'M A GHOST.
...WHIIIIT!!
HUFF HUFF
CELIA! COME BACK!
WHIT, STOP!! WHIT, PLEASE!
...
WISTY, I SAW CELIA.
WHAT? IN THE WALL?

K-CHIK
...SHADOW-LAND...
...CELIA... GHOST...
...WHAT?
WHAT?
STAND UP, YOU VERMIN. YOU'RE GOING BACK TO SEE JUDGE EZEKIEL UNGER.
!

FLIP FLIP
...
WISTERIA ALLGOOD. WHITFORD ALLGOOD.
I HAVE HERE YOUR MEDICAL REPORTS. YOUR TESTS HAVE COME BACK...

...NORMAL. EVERY SINGLE TEST!
!
I WANT TO KNOW RIGHT THIS INSTANT WHOM YOU BRIBED. WAS IT HIM? WAS IT THE VISITOR? I SUSPECT IT WAS HIM.
...!

BRIBED?! ARE YOU KIDDING??
OF COURSE YOU BRIBED SOMEONE! YOU'RE THE FARTHEST THING FROM NORMAL THERE IS!
BRIBED HIM WITH WHAT?! GRUEL? MICE DROPPINGS?!

YOU DON'T ASK THE QUESTIONS! YOU ANSWER THE QUESTIONS! FOR THE LAST TIME, WHO WAS IT? I KNOW IT WASN'T THE MATRON. SHE'S MY BELOVED SISTER.
—!

...?
ROACH, ROACH, YOU'RE A ROACH...
FLIES IN THE KITCHEN, LAWSY, MAWSY...
FLIES IN THE NIGHT, LAWSY MAY...
?
FLIES ON THE RIVER, LAWSY, MAWSY...
?
BZZ
FLIES AT FIRST LIGHT, LAWSY MAY...
BZZ
BZZ
BZZ
BZZ
BZZ
...HUH?
BZZ
BZZ
BZZ

BZZZ BZZZ
WHAT THE—?!
AAAA
STING
STING
AAAAA
BZZZ
BZZ
SIS, DID YOU DO THAT?
UM... SORT OF. MAYBE... YES?

BZZ
BZZ
HOW?
BZZ
I'M NOT SURE. I WAS JUST SO ANGRY, AND THERE WAS THIS SONG ABOUT FLIES, AND...
BZZ
BZ
POP
POP
POP
!!
GLANCE
WRIGGLE
SUCK
AAAAAA
THIS IS WORSE! THIS IS MUCH WORSE!!!

AAAAAAAAAAH
THE FLIES TURNED INTO LEECHES?!
I DIDN'T SAY ANYTHING ABOUT LEECHES!
PULL
PFLRT
THIS IS PROBABLY THE MOST REPULSIVE THING I'VE EVER SEEN. I KIND OF LIKE IT.
HEY, THEY'RE NOT ATTACKING US AT A—
ENOUGH OF THIS KINDERGARTEN NONSENSE.
SHAAAA

POP
NO MORE HORSEFLIES, NO MORE LEECHES...
POP
...NO MORE UNCIVIL DISTURBANCES OF ANY KIND!
NO

NOW, THERE WILL BE MORE TESTS, TESTS, TESTS, TESTS. UNTIL WE FIND THE ANSWER I'M LOOKING FOR, UNTIL WE SOLVE THE PUZZLE...
...OF THE POWER OF THE ALLGOODS.
TAKE THE PRISONERS BACK TO THE HOSPITAL! DOUBLE THEIR WORKLOAD, DOUBLE THE TESTS, DOUBLE THE DISCOMFORT.
I WANT ANSWERS!

PUSH
SLAM
SO, WE MEET AGAIN.
OH LOOK, IT'S THE LITTLE VISITOR-IN-TRAINING.
"WE MEET AGAIN"? THAT'S THE BEST YOU COULD COME UP WITH? I MEAN, CLICHÉ MUCH?
SHUT UP, WITCH!! OR I'LL TELL THE MATRON TO STUN-GUN YOU UNTIL YOU HAVE NO MORE ATTITUDE THAN A HEAD OF LETTUCE!

SMOOTH
NOW HEAR THIS. YOU BOTH HAVE BEEN DESIGNATED *EXTREMELY DANGEROUS* BY THE NEW ORDER.

WE'RE HONORED. WE'D LIKE TO THANK OUR PARENTS AND COACH—
A RATING OF EXTREMELY DANGEROUS LOWERS THE AGE FOR EXECUTION FROM EIGHTEEN DOWN TO... *ZERO.*
WHICH MEANS, LET ME SEE... BOTH OF YOU CAN NOW BE EXECUTED...

...TOMORROW.

!!

HA HA HA HA
WHAT, NO WIZARDLY WISECRACKS? BLACK CAT GOT YOUR TONGUE?
YOU THINK THAT'S FUNNY? WHAT IF WISTY WERE YOUR SISTER AND SHE WAS GOING TO BE EXECUTED TOMORROW?
MY SISTER WAS A TRAITOR TO THE NEW ORDER. AND...I... TURNED.... HER...*IN*.

POOF
UH.
!
I COULD SWEAR I SAID "PUMPKIN."
?
ROOOAR
AAAAAAA

CHANGE HIM BACK!! DO IT NOW! QUICK, QUICK, QUICK!!
U-UH, BIBBIDI-BOBBIDI-BOO!!
ROAR
WISTY!!
TURN INTO YOUR NATURAL FORM!
DO IT! DO IT—I'M SERIOUS!!
BOOM

...WHA...?
OH YEAH, THAT'S DEFINITELY MORE HIM. ANYTHING ELSE TO SAY, BYRON?
I THINK HE LIKED BEING A LION BETTER.
HSSS
SWING
WHAT WAS THAT AWFUL, TERRIBLE NOISE?
SOUNDED LIKE... A LION ROARING.
SKITTER SKITTER

A LION? HERE? IN OUR CELL?
...WHERE IS JUNIOR INFORMANT SWAIN?
I'M SORRY, BUT HE LEFT, MATRON. READ US THE ABRIDGED RIOT ACT, THOUGH. HE'S TOUGH.
LIES!!
SEARCH EVERY INCH OF THIS CELL!!
SEARCH
SEARCH
SEARCH

WIPE

I THINK YOU FORGOT TO CHECK IN THAT CRACK.

SHUT UP, VERMIN!!

HE'S NOT HERE, MATRON.

I CAN SEE THAT!!

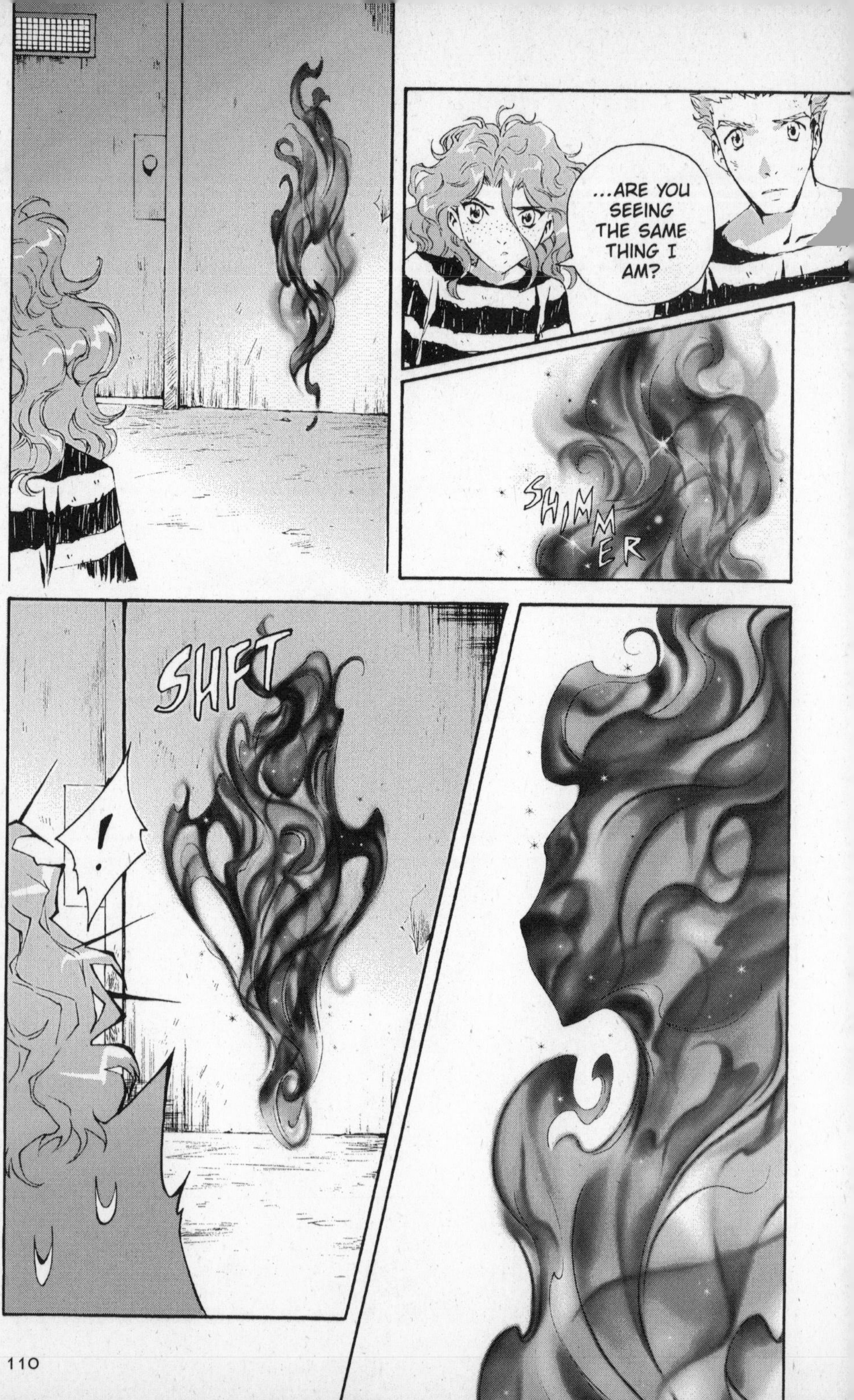

SHFT

!

HI, WHIT.
HI, WISTY.
...CELIA!!
I'VE COME TO BUST YOU OUT OF THIS WRETCHED HOSPITAL.

WITCH & WIZARD

CELIA! YOU CAME—

WHIT...

PASS

WHAT'S A HALF-LIGHT?
THE SHADOW-LAND? THAT GRAY PLACE WHERE I SAW YOU?
WE ARE... SPIRITS OF THOSE WHO'VE DIED. WE LIVE IN THE SHADOW-LAND.
YES. SORRY, THERE'S A LOT TO EXPLAIN...I WAS ABLE TO COME HERE THROUGH ONE OF THE PORTALS—THEY ARE HOLES BETWEEN THE TWO REALMS.
THEY APPEAR AND DISAPPEAR RANDOMLY, BUT WHILE THEY'RE THERE... HALF-LIGHTS AND CERTAIN PEOPLE AND ANIMALS—CALLED CURVES—CAN GO THROUGH THEM.
LIKE YOUR WEASEL DID.
!!
BYRON?
HE'S NOT *OUR* WEASEL. HE'S OUR ENEMY, ACTUALLY. A VICIOUS LITTLE SCUMBAG.

WELL, HE KNEW YOU.
HE TOLD US YOU'RE SCHEDULED TO BE EXECUTED TOMORROW.
...!
AT FIRST HE DIDN'T WANT TO TELL US ANYTHING, BUT WE HELD HIM UPSIDE DOWN AND TICKLED HIS LITTLE WEASEL BELLY UNTIL TEARS CAME OUT OF HIS EYES. BY THE END HE WAS BEGGING TO TELL US EVERYTHING. NOW HE DOESN'T WANT TO COME BACK HERE.
NOW WE'VE GOT TO HURRY. I CAN'T STAY IN YOUR WORLD MUCH LONGER, AND WE HAVE TO GET YOU BOTH OUT OF HERE AND TO THE UNDERWORLD.
THE UNDER-WORLD? WHERE IS THAT?
IT'S... EVERYWHERE THAT ISN'T THE OVERWORLD, WHICH IS THE REALITY YOU KNOW, CONTROLLED BY THE NEW ORDER.
THE REST OF THE KNOWN UNIVERSE IS CALLED THE UNDER-WORLD—THAT'S THE SHADOWLAND AND OTHER DIMENSIONS.

THE N.O. DOESN'T RUN THE SHOW IN THOSE PLACES. YET. BUT THEY'RE TRYING.
THE ONE WHO IS THE ONE IS AFTER TOTAL CONTROL.
SOMEHOW YOU TWO ARE IN HIS WAY.

OKAY, IT'S ALMOST TIME. YOU TWO HAVE TO DO EXACTLY WHAT I SAY, OKAY?
THE PORTAL IN YOUR BATHROOM IS GONE ALREADY, BUT WE FOUND A NEW ONE. ONCE WE GET THE DOOR OPEN, YOU HAVE TO RUN FOR IT.

OKAY, WE'RE READY. WHERE IS IT?
IT'S, UH...IT'S DOWN THE HALLWAY, PAST THE DOGS, UNFORTUNATELY...
WHOA, WHOA, NOT READY, NOT READY! PAST THE DOGS?

AND THERE'S NOTHING BUT A SOLID BRICK WALL AT THE END OF THAT HALLWAY!
WE HAVE TO RUN INTO A WALL...?
WISTY, WHIT, PLEASE, YOU HAVE TO TRUST ME.
YOU DO HAVE TO RUN INTO THE WALL, BUT YOU'LL GO THROUGH IT, I PROMISE.
WE HAVE NO TIME LEFT. WHIT, QUICK, RAP ON THE DOOR THREE TIMES!
BANG BANG BANG
CLICK
SHF
NOW, RUN!

SCREAM IF YOU HAVE TO, BUT DON'T STOP.
SCREAM. DON'T STOP. GOT IT.
AAAAAA!!!!
!!
ESCAPE ATTEMPT!! STOP THEM!! SOUND THE ALARM!!
SKIDD
BARK
BARK
SNARL
BARK

QUICK, DO YOUR STUFF AND TURN THEM INTO PUPPIES OR STUFFED TOYS OR SOMETHING!
UH, UH!
FREEZE!
BARK BARK
BARK
BRK...
FREEZE
...!

YES!! I'M A WITCH!!
PERFECT!! YOU'RE AMAZING, WISTY!
STOP, VERMIN! YOU HAVE NOWHERE TO RUN!!
WHIT, GO!! TRUST ME!

??
WISTY!!
RELEASE!
POP
POP
BARK
BARK
BARK

SNARL CHOMP
WISTY, LET'S GO!!
BARK
BARK
SNARL
IT WORKED!!
IT ACTUALLY WORKED!!
BARK BARK BA...
!!

WATCH OUT!
NO, NO, IT MUST BE OKAY—IT'S A CURVE DOG!
BARK?...
TURN
LOOK
SNF
A CURVE IS ANYONE WHO HAS ACCESS TO THE UNDERWORLD. THIS ONE MUST NOT HAVE BEEN FULLY BRAINWASHED BY THE STRAIGHT AND NARROWS.
WHINE
CRASH!!
SLIIIDE
AHHHH... NOT A CURVE?
NOPE.
DIDN'T THINK SO.

YESSS, WE'RE OUT!!!
WHINE...
COWER
...UH...
OH, GIVE IT A CHANCE, WISTY. LOOK HOW SORRY IT IS! I WISH I COULD PET IT...
WHINE
...
...D'AWWW!
IT'S A SHE. I'M GOING TO CALL HER FEFFER.
OKAY, YOU CAN COME WITH US.
WELL, I GUESS IT CAN BE A GUARD DOG OR SOMETHING.
WAG WAG
...

SO THIS IS THE SHADOW-LAND?
TURN
THERE'S... NOTHING HERE. THIS IS YOUR HOME?
I WOULD NEVER CALL THE SHADOWLAND HOME. AND I HOPE NEITHER OF YOU DO EITHER.
MOOOAN..
LET'S GET YOU SOME-WHERE SAFE. THE SHADOW-LAND CAN BE A VERY DANGEROUS PLACE FOR HUMANS.
WH-WHAT WAS THAT?
LOST ONES. THEY'RE NOT CLOSE YET, AND THAT'S THE WAY WE WANT TO KEEP IT.

OH, THERE YOU ARE!
CELIA, YOU'RE SAFE!
FREEDOM SHO BE

CAN'T YOU COME WITH US? AND STAY?
THIS IS SASHA. HE'LL HELP YOU GET TO THE FREELAND.
OF COURSE I'LL COME... BUT I CAN'T STAY. IF I STAY TOO LONG I'LL...
...CEASE TO BE.
...

?!?
YEAH, LET'S GET OUT OF HERE!
WE'D BETTER GET MOVING BEFORE ANY LOST ONES SPOT US. I THINK I HEARD A PACK NOT FAR FROM HERE.
FREEDOM SHOULD BE FREE

YOU TAUGHT A WEASEL HOW TO SPEAK?!

WHOA!

FSS!! NO! I WAS A HUMAN! SHE'S A WITCH.

THAT'S RIGHT, AND DON'T YOU FORGET IT.

FEFFER...

...MEET BYRON TRAITOR SUCK-UP. YOU MAY EAT HIM.

MOOOAAN

NAVY SEALS

NAVY SEALS

WE HAVE TO GO.

FREEDOM SHOULD BE FREE

THIS WAY. BE VERY QUIET.

RUN FOR IT!!
NO!

DA
DA
DA
WHERE'S THE PORTAL?!
IT'S JUST AHEAD!!
HA
GRAB
HOOWL
HHUH
HHUH
DA
DA
DA

!
SLIDE
SKIDD

KLIK
KLIK

KLIK
KLIK

KLIK

KLIK

KLIK

SASHA, NOW WHAT?!

WITCH & WIZARD

FREEDOM SHOULD BE FREE
RUSTLE
OKAY, LOOK, YOU GOT US. BUT LISTEN— THIS IS A MAP.
FREEDOM SHOULD BE FREE
NAVY SEALS
IT SHOWS WHERE TO FIND A PORTAL— NOT LIKE THIS ONE, WHICH WON'T WORK FOR YOUR KIND— THAT CAN TAKE YOU OUT OF THE SHADOWLAND.

A WAY BACK HOME.
CRUMPLE
CRUMPLE
TOSS
HOOWL
DASH
HISS HISS
HISS
GO!!

OOF!
PHEW! SORRY, DIDN'T MEAN TO SQUISH YOU LIKE THAT.
WAS THAT REALLY A MAP? WILL THEY BE ABLE TO GET OUT NOW?

NAH, IT WAS JUST A LIST OF THINGS I HAD TO DO. BESIDES, I DON'T THINK THEY CAN READ.
FREEDOM
EEEEEE
NAVY SEALS
FREED
EEEEEEE
!
NAVY SEALS
INCOMING!! EVERYONE GET DOWN!
EEEE
KBOOM

WHAT WAS THAT??
BOMB. GUESS WE STEPPED INTO A WAR ZONE. EASY TO DO.

THE NEW ORDER RUNS AIR STRIKES EVERY DAY. THEY KNOW SOME OF US KIDS ARE SQUATTING HERE.

THE N.O. IS TAKING OVER "WORTHY" COMMUNITIES AND SHAPING EVERYTHING IN ITS IMAGE. THE REST, THEY'RE JUST...RAZING. LIKE, TOTALING OUT OF EXISTENCE.

SO THEY BOMB AND THEN COME LOOKING FOR US. KEEPS YOU ON YOUR TOES, RIGHT?
...
YEAH, NOTHING LIKE A BIT OF SHOCK AND AWE.
EEEEEEEEEEE
KBOOM
!!

WE HAVE TO GET THEM TO FREELAND RIGHT AWAY.
RIGHT.
COME ON, FOLLOW ME!
EEEEEEEKBOOM
GARFUNKEL
HERE WE GO! HOME SWEET RUBBLE-STREWN HOME.
!!

YOU LIVE AT GARFUN-KEL'S?!

YOU KNOW IT?

YEAH, IT'S ONLY THE MOST AMAZING LUXURY DEPARTMENT STORE IN THE WHOLE WORLD. I'D NEVER BEEN ABLE TO AFFORD TO EVEN WALK THROUGH THE DOORS.

WELL, THIS IS WHERE A BUNCH OF US ARE HANGING OUT. THE PLACE WAS KIND OF A MESS, BUT WE'VE FIXED IT UP PRETTY GOOD.

SASHA, IS THAT YOU?! YOU'RE ALIVE!
HEY! YEAH, STILL! HA-HA!
I WONDER HOW LONG I'VE BEEN GONE FOR...
WHAT DO YOU MEAN?
YOU HAVEN'T TOLD THEM?
I DIDN'T GET TO EXPLAIN EVERYTHING. WE WERE KIND OF BUSY ESCAPING, YOU KNOW.
TIME IS DIFFERENT IN THE SHADOWLAND, AND DOESN'T ALWAYS EQUAL THE TIME HERE. IN THIS CASE, IT LOOKS LIKE I'VE BEEN GONE ABOUT A MONTH...
...EVEN THOUGH IT'S ONLY BEEN A FEW HOURS FOR ME. IT'S NOT CONSIS-TENT. DEPENDS ON THE PORTAL YOU HAVE TO USE.
MANAGER
...AHA!

WE'VE GOT OUR OWN LITTLE PUKKA SOCIETY HERE.
NAVY SEALS
FREEDOM SHOULD BE FREE
INCLUDING, TA-DAH! THIS WEEK'S LEADER. MEET MY FORMER BASIC-COMBAT PARTNER, JANINE.
AND THAT'S JONATHAN. HEY, MAN.
HEY.
SASHA, IT'S BEEN, WHAT, FORTY-THREE DAYS? WE NEEDED YOU HERE.
HEY, CELIA AND I HAD AN OPERATION TO RUN! WHICH WAS HUGELY SUCCESSFUL, I MUST ADD. JANINE, MEET WHIT AND WISTY.
HI. WELCOME.
I HAVE TO GO NOW, MY TIME IS ALMOST DONE.
UNDERSTOOD. WE'LL TAKE IT FROM HERE.
WHIT, I'LL TRY TO COME BACK...
CELIA, WAIT A SECOND!

OVER HERE.
WHAT DO PEOPLE MEAN BY "THIS WEEK'S LEADER"?
...
...PLEASE COME BACK.
I CAN'T STAND TO LOSE YOU AGAIN.
I WILL TRY, WHIT. I WANT TO. I'M SO GLAD YOU'RE ALIVE.
OUT OF EVERYTHING I MISS...
...I'VE MISSED YOU THE MOST.
OH GOD, I'VE MISSED YOU.

GOOD-BYE, WHIT.
SNIFF

...GROWN-UPS HAVE AMPLY DEMONSTRATED THAT POWER CORRUPTS.

BUT YOU DO NEED ONE PERSON IN CHARGE, A FINAL DECISION-MAKER, OR ELSE EVERYTHING GOES CRAZY. SO WE HAVE A LEADER, BUT IT CHANGES EVERY WEEK. THIS IS MY WEEK.

I'M SORRY, BUT WE CAN'T STAY HERE. WE HAVE TO FIND OUR PARENTS. THEY'RE IN DANGER.

GRAB
YOU HAVE TO HELP US.
IT'S THE NEW ORDER REFORMATORY, THE SAME PLACE YOU WERE TAKEN AFTER YOU WERE KIDNAPPED. IT'S AN EVIL PLACE.

WE'VE BEEN THERE. WE KNOW HOW BAD IT IS. BUT YOU HAVE TO UNDERSTAND, FAMILY COMES FIRST FOR US.

YOU SAY YOU KNOW HOW BAD IT IS, BUT YOU HAVE NO IDEA. YOU HAVEN'T SEEN EVEN HALF OF IT.

WE HAVE A BOY HERE, MICHAEL CLANCY. HE WAS LIKE YOU, MARKED "EXTREMELY DANGEROUS." HIM AND ABOUT FORTY OTHERS.

THE GUARDS JUST MARCHED THEM OUT INTO THE PRISON YARD ONE MORNING. A BUNCH OF KIDS, ALL STARVED, ALL TIRED. BROKEN.
THERE WAS A GREAT WIND, AND THEN THE ONE WHO IS THE ONE WAS RIGHT IN FRONT OF THEM, LOOKING AT THEM WITH DISDAIN. HE SAID NOTHING... HE JUST... FLICKED HIS WRIST.
AND THERE WAS NOTHING LEFT OF THEM, EXCEPT FOR SMOKE...
...AND THE SMELL OF SKIN BURNING.

MICHAEL ALONE WAS SPARED. HE DOESN'T KNOW WHY.
HE'S HERE NOW.
WE MANAGED TO RESCUE HIM. BUT THERE'RE MANY OTHERS IN THE OVERWORLD PRISON, AND WE NEED YOUR HELP.
...THE RAID IS TOMORROW? DO YOU KNOW HOW THE JAIL'S LAID OUT? NOT THAT WE'RE COMMITTING. WE CAN'T DO THAT.
WE HAVE THE SCHEMATICS, YES.
TAP
TAP
WAVE
YOU SHOULD ALSO KNOW SOME BACKGROUND, SO JONATHAN WILL TAKE YOU TO SEE THE NEW ORDER'S FIRST STRONGHOLD.

BUT FIRST, I'D LIKE YOU TO MEET SOMEONE.
YEAH?
JAMILLA, THIS IS WIZARD ALLGOOD AND HIS SISTER, WITCH ALLGOOD.
THE SHAMAN. IN OTHER WORDS, AN ODDBALL LIKE YOU TWO, EXCEPT I DON'T DO MAGIC.
I JUST HELP OTHER PEOPLE DO CANTRIPS, HELPING THEM HONE THEIR POWERS.
HI. I'M THE SHAMAN.
...THE HUH?

TURN
THERE'S A RANGE.
SOME PEOPLE KNOW WHO'S CALLING ON THE PHONE, OTHERS CAN ACTUALLY MAKE SMALL OBJECTS FLOAT IN THE AIR. SOME CAN EVEN SAY WHAT'S IN YOUR POCKETS OR PURSE.

BUT I'M VERY CURIOUS ABOUT WHAT YOU TWO CAN DO. NEW ORDER'S BEEN SPENDING CRAZY RESOURCES ON YOU, WE'VE NEVER SEEN ANYTHING LIKE IT.

WELL, WE CAN DO SOME MAGIC, BUT IT'S HARD TO CONTROL.
LIKE WHAT?
LIKE THIS.

FOOM
HEH
SHOW-OFF.
POOF!
!!
YES!! I DID IT!! I PUT MYSELF OUT!!
HIGH-FIVE, SISTER. YOU THE WITCH!
YOU DID THAT ON PURPOSE?
YEAH, TOTALLY! USUALLY IT HAPPENS BY ACCIDENT—SOMEONE HAS TO GET ME REALLY TICKED OFF...
...AND THEN GET A FIRE EXTINGUISHER.
WHAT ELSE CAN YOU DO?

WELL, WHIT STUCK A HAND THROUGH A WALL. AND STOPPED A GAVEL IN MIDAIR.
I SOMETIMES FLOAT WHEN I SLEEP, UH, UNINTENTIONALLY, AND I FROZE A BUNCH OF GUARD DOGS AT THE HOSPITAL.

NOD
THE LEECHES TOO, IN THE COURTROOM.
OH YEAH! I MADE A BUNCH OF HORSEFLIES. EVEN THOUGH I WAS ACTUALLY TRYING TO TURN THAT JUDGE INTO A COCKROACH...
POP!
AND THEN THERE'S LITTLE OLE ME.

UGH. YEAH.
SHOO
HE USED TO BE A HUMAN. BUT THIS IS HIS TRUE FORM.
MY TRUE FORM WAS THE LION.

GAPE
...WHAT?

OH MY GOD. I THINK THIS IS THEM.
THEM WHO?
THE LIBERATORS. THE RESCUERS. THERE'S A PROPHECY—AND IT'S ABOUT THE TWO OF YOU!
!
DASH
CHECK THIS OUT.
A BLANK WALL?
NO, NO, GIVE IT MINUTE. IT DOESN'T ALWAYS DO IT.

...
THIS IS THE PROPHECY WALL. MESSAGES APPEAR ON IT. USUALLY IT'S RANDOM STORE STUFF, LIKE "HUGE SALE IN JANUARY."
BUT SOMETIMES IT'S "GO TO FIFTH STREET. RESCUE AN ORPHAN KID FROM HOUSE NUMBER TWENTY-FOUR," THINGS LIKE THAT.
AH! THERE!!

ONE DAY SOON, KIDS WILL RUN THE WORLD... AND DO A BETTER JOB THAN GROWN-UPS EVER DID.

FREEDOM SHOULD

. . .

...WHOA, HEAVY.

Witch & Wizard

BED & BAT

Z Z Z Z

SCRIBBLE SCRIBBLE

WE'RE SUPPOSED TO BE RESTING. WHAT ARE YOU DOING?
MAKING A REVIEW LIST OF WHAT'S HAPPENED. NINE W.T.H. ITEMS SO FAR...AND COUNTING.

1 I am witch. A witch!! Whit is a wizard
We don't exactly know how to control our powers.
2 Whit and I were sentenced to death by an insidious individual named The One Who Is The One.
3 My parents are wanted for treason and we still have no idea where they are. Or whether they are still alive.
4 We were tortured in a "magic-dampening" prison.
5 A dead girl, who happen to be the true love of Whit's life, rescued us from there.
6 I turned Byron Swain into a weasel. THAT I'm proud of.
...THAT IS A LOT TO DEAL WITH...
. . .

REMEMBER WHEN GETTING GROUNDED WAS OUR DEFINITION OF "BAD"?
YEAH...
I'M JUST... I'M STILL STUCK ON NUMBER THREE, WHIT.
individual named
Is The One.
3. My parents are wanted for treason and we still have no idea where they are. Or whether they are still alive.
4 We were tortured in a "magic-

...
OKAY, READY FOR YOUR TOUR OF THE ENEMY CAMP?
YEAH. WHERE ARE WE GOING AGAIN?
THE CITY OF PROGRESS—THE NEW ORDER'S IDEAL COMMUNITY. IT'S KIND OF THE FLOOR MODEL FOR WHAT THEY WANT TO CARPET THE ENTIRE PLANET WITH.
YOU'LL NEED DISGUISES. EMMET WILL HELP YOU WITH THOSE.
...DISGUISES?
DON'T WORRY—I'M *VERY* GOOD.
FOLLOW ME, YOU TWO! FIRST, WE GO TO COSMETICS TO DO YOUR MAKEUP.
WAIT, WHAT?

WELCOME TO
CITY of PROGRESS
OKAY, BE ON YOUR GUARD. WE CANNOT GET ARRESTED HERE.
N.O.
N.O.
N.O.
N.O.
N.O.
N.O.
SAY N.O. TO ART
ONE SMALL MISTAKE AND WE'RE TOAST. THE PLACE IS FULL OF ERLENMEYERS.
IF YOU SEE SOMET
SAY SOMETHI
?
UM, JONATHAN, THESE DISGUISES...
BOWS
COMBED
N.O.
ARE YOU SURE THEY ARE NECESSARY?
WAG
WAG

N.C
ABSOLUTELY. WE NEED TO BLEND IN.
OTHERWISE, YOU KNOW... OFF WITH YOUR HEADS!

YOU LOOK LIKE A POSTER BOY FOR THE NATIONAL GUARD.
YOU LOOK LIKE...A *GIRL*.
MINUS THE CHEST.

OH YEAH? WELL, YOU...
SHHH!

TURN
HA-HA, HOW DO YOU DO?
NO *CANTRIPS!* DON'T EVEN *THINK* ABOUT IT.
SORRY.

N.O
IF YOU HAVE TO TALK TO ANYONE, REMEMBER TO SMILE AND SAY "MA'AM" OR "SIR."
DO NOT CROSS THE STREET AGAINST THE LIGHT, DO NOT SNAP GUM IN PUBLIC, AND FOR GOD'S SAKE...
PROUD PARENT OF A NEW ORDER JUNIOR INFORMANT
...DO NOT LET THAT DOG DO HER BUSINESS. ALL DOGS IN THE CITY OF PROGRESS ARE TRAINED TO USE LITTER BOXES INDOORS, JUST LIKE CATS.
WHINE
NEW ORDER INFORMANT CENTER
WOW... EVERYTHING SMELLS LIKE FRESH PAINT.
der DINER
OH GOODNESS, THEY KEPT THE DINERS!
GROWL

N.O.
YES? HELP YOU FOLKS?

GOSH, MISTER, IT'S HARD TO DECIDE.

N.O.

MAY I PLEASE HAVE A ROOT-BEER FLOAT AND THE CHEESEBURGER DELUXE? THANK YOU.

...DO YOU FEEL ANY-THING... ODD?

...

...YES. THAT LADY WITH THE TWO OTHERS. THEY'RE WATCHING US.
WHAT SHOULD WE D—
SHE'S A WITCH.
WHAT DID YOU SAY, MRS. HIGH-SMITH?
THAT OBNOXIOUSLY RED-HAIRED GIRL THERE. SHE'S A WITCH.
AND THAT BLOND BOY, THE HANDSOME ONE, THERE'S SOMETHING NOT RIGHT ABOUT HIM EITHER.

TURN!
A WITCH?! WHERE?
THIS GIRL WAS JUST NAMED SECTOR LEADER'S STAR OF HONOR.
MY SISTER IS CERTAINLY NOT A WITCH!
MAYBE... MAYBE MRS. HIGHSMITH IS IMAGINING THINGS?
MAYBE SHE... SEES THINGS?
MRS. HIGHSMITH, DO YOU HAVE VISIONS?
...!

I'D BE HAPPY TO TAKE A TEST.
IF YOU TAKE ONE TOO.
JUST TEST HER!

....!
NO
IT'S NOT ME, IT'S HER!

GLANCE

LIFT
AAAAAAA
HELP! HELP!
ZOOM
STAB
SHE'S TRYING TO HURT ME!! HOW IS SHE DOING THAT?!
!
DID YOU SEE THAT? HER FORK, IT FLEW! IT'S UNNATURAL!
!
CALL SECURITY SERVICES! SHE HURT THAT STAR OF HONOR GIRL.
GET HER!
SHE IS A WITCH!
COME ON, GUYS, WE'RE DONE HERE. LET'S REPORT THIS PLACE!

LOOK

!!
PUSH
AAAAAAAAAA
POOF
POOF

A COVEN. THAT WAS A COVEN OF WITCHES.
WAY TO *NOT* ATTRACT ATTENTION.
N.O.
SAY NO
GARFUNKEL'
MUSS MUSS
THAT WAS... INTERESTING.
WELCOME BACK.
MEET MARGO, SHE'S THE TEAM LEADER FOR THE BREAK-IN.

WE'VE JUST GOTTEN A MESSAGE FROM OUR SPIES MONITORING THE OVERWORLD PRISON. MORE EXTERMINATIONS ARE SCHEDULED FOR TOMORROW MORNING. VAPORIZATION.

...!

BUT THERE'S SOME-THING ELSE...

YOUR PARENTS HAVE BEEN CAPTURED AGAIN.
WHAT?!
N.D.
WHERE ARE THEY? WHEREVER THEY ARE, WE'RE THERE. EFFECTIVE IMMEDIATELY.
SORRY WE CAN'T HELP YOU, SASHA.
NAVY SEALS
NO NEED TO APOLOGIZE. IN FACT, YOUR PARENTS ARE BEING HELD AT OVERWORLD.
....!
WE'RE IN.
NOD

WITCH & WIZARD

THIS WAY.

TAP
TAP
TAP
WE'VE GOT TWO MORE BLOCKS TO GO...
...AND IT'S ONLY A FEW MINUTES UNTIL SHIFT CHANGE.

WOW. THAT'S SO COOL.

NOW, ME.

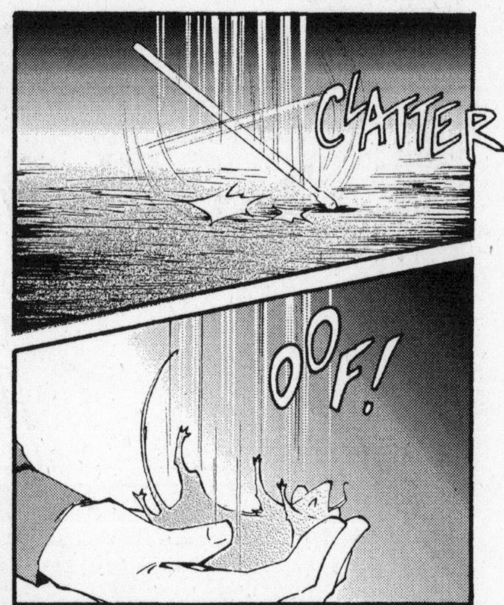

A MOUSE?! THAT WAS YOUR BRILLIANT PLAN FOR YOURSELF?!! I CAN'T LET YOU GO LIKE THIS!!

WHIT, I'LL BE FINE, I PROMISE!!

YOU ALMOST WENT SPLAT ON THE PAVEMENT! WHAT IF SOME-ONE SQUASHES YOU? THIS IS NOT A GOOD IDEA!

NO, LISTEN, LISTEN—A MOUSE CAN SNEAK IN UNNOTICED ANYWHERE, CHEW THROUGH WIRES, OR CRAWL THROUGH SKINNY PIPES.

THERE'S A BETTER CHANCE I'LL FIND MOM AND DAD LIKE THIS!

...
COME ON, WHIT, I CAN DO THIS!

SIS...
LOOK AT HOW SMALL I AM! THEY WON'T EVEN KNOW I'M THERE!

...
I HOPE YOU'RE RIGHT ABOUT THIS.
NOD
YES.
MARGO, PLEASE TAKE MY DRUMSTICK, AND KEEP IT SAFE.

LET'S GO.

N.O. REFORMATORY

OKAY, YOU'RE CLEAR, GO IN.

WHAT'S THAT? WHAT HAPPENED?

SOME KIDS! THEY RAN THAT WAY!!

OKAY, THE LULLABY SPELL MOM AND DAD USED ON US. TOGETHER, LIKE WE PRACTICED.
SLEEP NOW, LITTLE ONES, REST YOUR HEADS AND SLEEP.
THE NIGHT WILL HOLD YOU IN ITS ARMS...

...AND SAFELY YOU WILL KEEP.

WHAT'S YOUR NAME, BUB?
YOU'RE NEW HERE, AREN'T YOU? HAVEN'T SEEN YOU AROUND BEFORE.
UH, WILL. WILLIAM.
HIDE

SLEEP. SLEEP. SLEEEEEP.

WILL WILLIAM, HUH?

LET'S SEE SOME IDENTIFI—

FWUMP

WHIT, I CAN DO THIS. GET THESE KIDS TO SAFETY.
WISTY, I CAN'T JUST LEAVE—
. . .
OKAY, BUT IF YOU SEE CHUNKS OF CHEESE, LIKE, IN THE MIDDLE OF A SMALL WOODEN BOARD, WITH WIRE—
I GOT IT, I GOT IT!
WHIT, I'LL BE FINE, I PROMISE!!
JUMP
SEE? I DIDN'T GO SPLAT!
JUST BE CAREFUL, SIS. WE'LL BE STANDING BY.
"CAREFUL" IS MY MIDDLE NAME!
SCRP
SCRP

WHERE'S WISTY?

UP A DRAINPIPE. WHERE ELSE?

WE HAVE TO GET THE KIDS TO SAFETY. WHICH WAY AM I GOING?

QUICK, TAKE A RIGHT AT THIS LIGHT!

SKREEEE
AAAAAAAAAA!!
OKAY, NEXT?
RIGHT, YEAH, SEE THAT BIG SIGN? SHARP LEFT AFTER IT.
WAIT, WHAT? THERE'S NO TURN THERE, IT'S A CURB!
TRUST ME, IT'S A SHORTCUT! JUST TURN!
HANG ON, EVERYBODY! THIS COULD GET A LITTLE ROUGH!
HOP
ARE YOU NUTS?! THERE'S NOTHING THER—

SUBWAY

...UH.

GACHONK

AAAA

AAAAA

GACHONK

WHAT WERE YOU THINKING?? THIS IS A SUBWAY STATION!!
CRASH
IT'S ABANDONED! WE CAN RIDE THE TRACKS ALL THE WAY TO THE PORTAL BACK HOME TO GARFUNKEL'S!
EVERYONE HANG ON!!
SKIDD

KA-CHONK
AAAAAA

. . .

FWEEEEEEEE

...OH GOD.

AAAA

AAAA

DRIVE!!!

O. REFORMATORY

...

...THE SCHEMATICS DIDN'T HAVE THIS PIPE.

SNIFF SNIFF

POP!
...!!
AAAAAAA
AAAA
LEVITATE!!
LEVITATE!!
AAAAA
FWAP

?
KRK KRK
SNAP
AAAAAAA!
?
HSS HSS HSS HSS
...!
HSS HSSS

AAAAAAA!!
BITE
SNAP
HSSS
HSS
HSS
POP
UGH, GET OFF!!
SKITTER
SKITTER

PANT
CLICK
!!

ESCAPEE!! SOUND THE ALARM!!
PUSH
BREEE BREEE
BREEE
BREEE

!!

HHUF
HHUF

STOP! COME BACK! YOU'LL KILL YOURSELF!
ALMOST THERE, ALMOST THERE.

TMP
TMP
TMP
STUMBLE
!
AAAAAAA

WITCH & WIZARD

FFWEEEEEEE
DRIVE, WHIT!!
IT WON'T START!!
GNNHK
FWEEEEEE
AAAAAAA
GNNHK
COME ON!

AAAAAAAAA
WE HAVE TO GET OUT OF THE VAN!
WHIT, DRIVE!!
NO, WE HAVE NOWHERE ELSE TO GO!!
TURN

VROOOM
VRRN
GO GO GO!!!
YEAH!!
CLONK CLONK
LURCH
CLONK

FLOOR IT! THE TURNOFF TUNNEL IS JUST AHEAD!!
WHICH ONE IS THE TRAIN GOING TO TAKE?!
...!
FWEEEEEEE
I...I HAVE NO IDEA.
OKAY, OKAY! I THINK I KNOW WHAT TO DO!
SWITCH
KRK KRK

FWEEEEEEEE

KLAKETA

ZOOM

KLAKETA

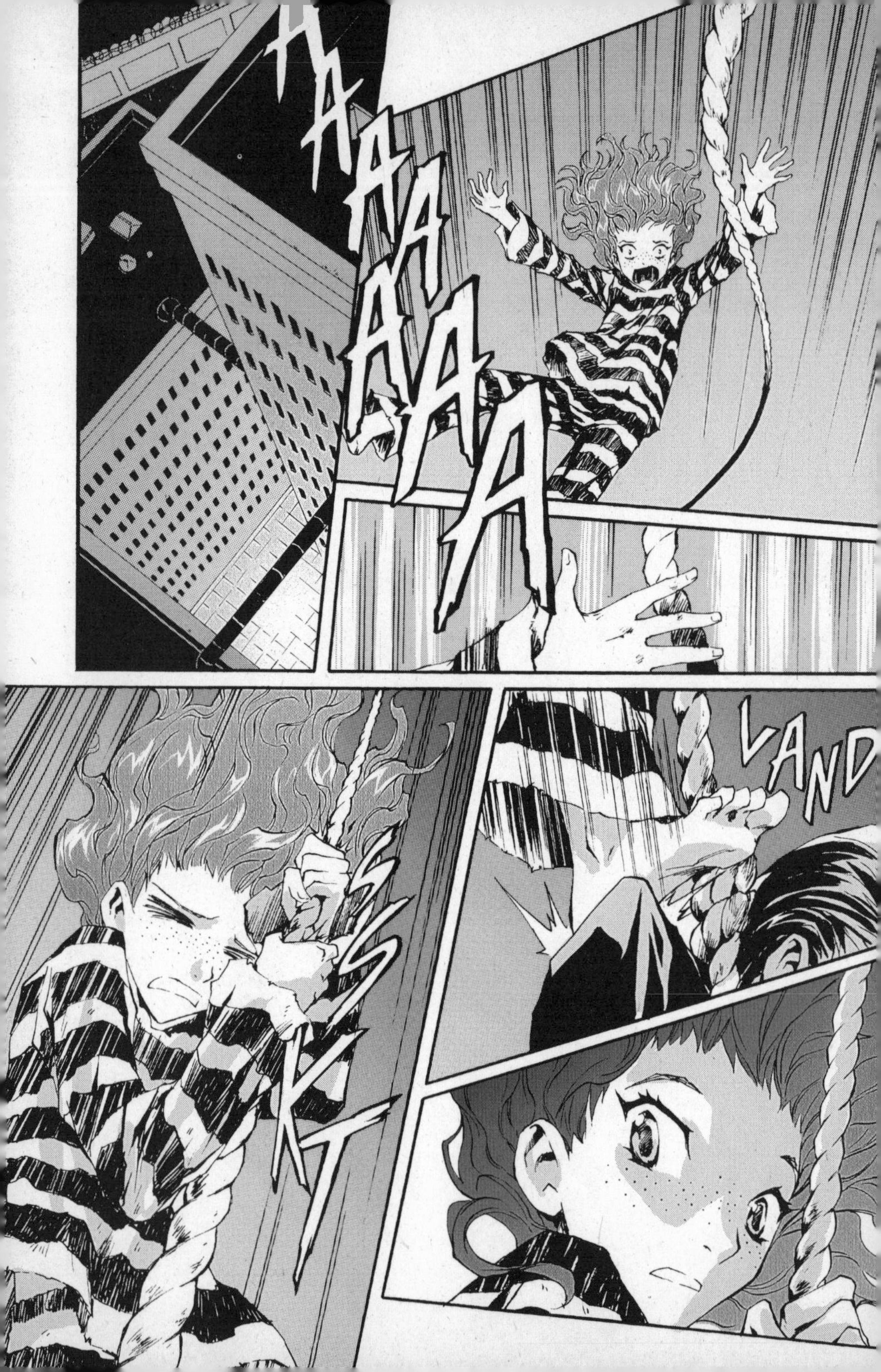

HAAAAAAA

LAND

SSKT

AAAAAAA
THUD
NNGH
FAILED TO PREVENT THE ESCAPE OF DANGEROUS NEW ORDER ENEMIES.
....!

TURN

NNGH...

WOBBLE

YANK

NOBODY. EVER. ESCAPES!

GARFUNKEL'S
WHIT, YOU CHANGED BACK.
...YEAH.

DID THE SPELL WEAR OFF? OR DID WISTY...
...

WE HAVE TO GET BACK THERE.
OKAY, LET'S MOVE!

PUSH
WISTERIA ALLGOOD, WHAT LUCK! AND HERE WE THOUGHT IT WAS JUST A REGULAR PRISONER WE'D CAUGHT. NOW ALL WE HAVE TO DO IS FIND YOUR BROTHER...
...AND YOUR PARENTS, AND THE ALLGOOD THREAT WILL BE HISTORY.
MY PARENTS AREN'T IN THIS PRISON?!
WHY WOULD WE PUT YOUR PARENTS IN A CHILDREN'S PRISON?
OR WHY, INDEED, KEEP THEM ALIVE AT ALL? YOU, WE NEED TO INTERROGATE, BUT THEM...TRUST ME, AS SOON AS WE HAVE THEM, YOU CAN OFFICIALLY CALL YOURSELF AN ORPHAN.

PUT HER IN CELL BLOCK D, CELL FOUR TWELVE. SHE'S TOO DRAINED TO MAKE TROUBLE.

CLANG
JINGLE JINGLE
NNGH
HHUH
HHUH
TOUCH

I FAILED.
I LOST ALL
MY MAGIC. I
TRIED, BUT I
COULDN'T...

DON'T
CRY.

REMEMBER,
THEY'RE
AFRAID OF YOU.
THEY'RE AFRAID
OF ALL OF US.

THAT'S WHY
THEY'RE DOING
THIS.

...!

THEY KNOW WE
CAN CHANGE
EVERYTHING.

...
YOU ARE AFRAID.

...YOU SHOULD BE.

FREEZE!!!
...

I SAID SHUT IT!
CRACK
STAGGER
UGH...

TWITCH
TWITCH

FREEZE

HA HA HA

YOINK
YOU GUYS WANT TO GET OUT OF HERE OR WHAT?!

YEAH!
YEAH!
MOVE
!!
CLICK
...HUH?
WHY, YOU LITTLE...!
!!

GRRR
?!
BEEP
BEEP
CLICK
CLICK
SLIDE
SLIDE
SLIDE

HUH?! WHY ARE ALL THE DOORS OPENING?? DID YOU—
HA HA HA HA
THIS JAIL WASN'T BUILT BY THE N.O.!! THE BUILDERS ACTUALLY VALUED HUMAN LIVES. WHICH MEANS ALL THE CELL DOORS WILL AUTOMATICALLY OPEN...
...IN CASE OF FIRE.
BOO!! I'M A BAD, SCARY WITCH!!!
AAAAAAAA

EVERYBODY OUT!! GO TO THE STAIRCASE, THEN DOWN AND OUTSIDE!! TELL EVERYONE YOU SEE!! GO, GO, GO!! THEY'RE AFRAID OF YOU!!
STAY BACK!!
WHAT'S GOING ON??
!!
YOU COME NEAR ME...
...AND I WON'T GIVE YOU A CHOICE BETWEEN REGULAR AND EXTRACRISPY!

SCREEEE
SHE DID IT.
HURRY! WE'VE SET UP AN ESCAPE ROUTE THROUGH THE SEWERS. THAT WAY!

WISTY!!
WISTY, WHERE ARE YOU?!
STAGGER
...WHIT, YOU CA...
WISTY!!

IS SHE OKAY?!
GET THE VAN! WE'RE GETTING HER OUT OF HERE!!
NOD
OKAY!
I DON'T THINK SO, WIZARD.
N.O.
N.O.
N.O.
N.O.
N.O

I SEE THE INFORMATION ABOUT THE BREAKOUT WAS CORRECT.
GOOD JOB...
...JUNIOR INFORMANT JONATHAN.
N.O.
JON...? WHY...
SHRUG
IT'S TOO HARD, AND HOPELESS, LIVING LIKE YOU DO.
THE NEW ORDER OFFERS A BETTER LIFE. IT BEATS PRISON AND DEATH. I BELIEVE IN THE ONE.

YOU HAVE NOWHERE TO GO, WIZARD AND WITCH! YOU WILL NOW BE PUT TO DEATH AT ONCE.
...YOU'RE AFRAID OF US.

THEY'RE AFRAID OF CHANGE...
...AND WE MUST CHANGE.
THEY'RE AFRAID OF THE YOUNG, AND WE'RE THE YOUNG.
THEY'RE AFRAID OF BOOKS, AND KNOWLEDGE, AND IDEAS.
THEY'RE MOST AFRAID OF OUR MAGIC.
THEY'RE AFRAID OF CHANGE, AND WE MUST CHANGE.
THEY'RE AFRAID OF THE YOUNG, AND WE'RE THE YOUNG.

THEY'RE AFRAID OF BOOKS, AND KNOWLEDGE, AND IDEAS.
THEY'RE AFRAID OF EVERY-THING.
THEY'RE MOST AFRAID OF—
SILENCE!! SILENCE!! THE WITCH AND WIZARD MUST NOW BE PUT TO DEATH IMMEDIATELY!
YOU! TAKE THEM BACK INTO THE PRISON AND LOCK ALL THE DOORS!
LET THEM BURN!
THIS FIRE WILL TAKE CARE OF OUR SOCIETY'S PROBLEM ONCE AND FOR ALL!

NO!
WISTY...!
WOBBLE
YOU SAY YOU ARE THE ONE. BUT YOUR FORM WILL NOW *BECOME UNDONE.*
...!
WE'RE A WITCH AND WIZARD, AS YOU CAN CLEARLY TELL.
BUT SINCE YOU DON'T DESERVE...
...WHERE YOU PRESENTLY DWELL, IT IS NOW WITH GREAT PLEASURE WE SEND YOU OFF TO—

...UM.
ROACHLAND.
WHERE YOU WILL BE JUDGED A HEINOUS CRIMINAL EVEN UNDER THE LAWS OF ROACHES!
I GIVE YOU ALL MY POWER. YOU SPEAK FOR BOTH OF US.
EEEEEEEEEEEE

......!!
...
YOU'RE NEXT.
DASH!
YEAH! YEAH!
TROMP
TROMP
TROMP

SKITTER

SKITTER

!!

HSS

HSS

CRUNCH

YOU KNOW, I LIKE RATS *MUCH* BETTER WHEN THEY'RE NOT BIGGER THAN ME.

SWAY

THEY'RE ALMOST CUTE, DON'T YOU THINK?

FAINT

...!

SHE'S GOOD, WHITFORD.

SHE'S *VERY* GOOD. YOU BOTH ARE.
OF COURSE, YOU MUST KNOW THAT I HAD NO INTENTION OF LETTING EITHER OF YOU BE SERIOUSLY HARMED. NO, NO, NO.
...I'LL BET YOU DIDN'T.
I ABSOLUTELY DIDN'T. THAT ISN'T ONE OF THE PROPHECIES. EVEN I CAN'T CHANGE THOSE.

THE PROPHECIES ABOUT YOU AND YOUR SISTER, OF COURSE! YOU TRULY DO NOT KNOW THEM? YOUR PARENTS DIDN'T TELL YOU? NO ONE HAS?
WHAT PROPHECIES?!
OH WHIT, WHIT, POOR WHIT... ALL RIGHT THEN, I'LL HAVE TO BE THE BEARER OF LEGEND AND MYTH. LISTEN WELL.
PROPHECY ONE: A BOY AND GIRL, BROTHER AND SISTER, SHALL BE BORN TO WICCANS AND SHALL ACHIEVE POWERS HERETOFORE UNREALIZED BY ANY OTHER WICCANS.
PROPHECY TWO: THE BOY AND GIRL SHALL LEAD AN ARMY OF CHILDREN TO VICTORY...
AND LOOK AROUND. YOU WON THE BATTLE OF NEW ORDER REFORMATORY, DIDN'T YOU?
THREE: THE BROTHER AND SISTER SHALL KNOW GREAT SAD-NESS, SUFFERING, AND TERRIBLE BETRAYAL.

FOUR:
THEY MUST VISIT ALL FIVE LEVELS OF REALITY, WHICH NO ONE BEFORE THEM HAS DONE, AND LEARN THE LESSONS OF EACH LEVEL.
PROPHECY FIVE...
...WELL, I'LL COME BACK TO THAT ONE.
SIX:
ULTIMATELY, THE BROTHER AND SISTER SHALL COMBINE WITH AN EVEN GREATER POWER FOR THE GOODNESS AND PROSPERITY OF ALL.
...
SOUNDS EXCITING, NO?
SO, WHITFORD, WHAT DO YOU THINK OF ALL THIS? AM I A FRIEND OR FOE—OR A LITTLE OF EACH?
ARE THE IMPORTANT THINGS BLACK AND WHITE, OR MAYBE A LITTLE GRAY? DO FAIRIES, ELVES, AND GREMLINS EXIST? AND WILL YOU EVER SEE CELIA AGAIN?

AND THIS ONE LAST PROPHECY, SWEET PRINCE...
SSHAAAA
THE ALLGOODS SHALL BE EXECUTED. THAT IS PROPHECY FIVE.
GIVE MY BEST TO YOUR SISTER.
WAKE HER GENTLY.

WITCH & WIZARD

LICK
LICK

LICK
LICK

WISTY!
YOU'RE AWAKE!

...WHAT HAPPENED?
DON'T YOU REMEMBER? THE PRISON, JUDGE UNGER, THE MATRON, ALL THE KIDS?

I DO! WELL, MOST OF IT, I THINK.
YOU MISSED THE ONE WHO IS THE ONE.
I DID? HOW? WHEN?
I'LL TELL YOU LATER.

WHAT ABOUT MOM AND DAD? WHAT HAPPENED? WHERE ARE THEY?

...ASK HIM.
HE LIED TO US. MOM AND DAD WERE NEVER IN THE PRISON. HE LIED TO GET US TO HELP.
...!
I'LL NEVER FORGIVE YOU!

SHRUG
WORSE THINGS HAVE HAPPENED TO ME. FAR WORSE.
WE NEEDED YOU GUYS. THIS IS A WAR AGAINST TRUE EVIL. THE ENDS JUSTIFY ANY EFFECTIVE MEANS.
YOU USED OUR FRIENDSHIP AND RUINED IT FOREVER!! I SHOULD TURN YOU INTO A SLUG!
EASY, YOU'VE BEEN OUT FOR HOURS. HE'S NOT WORTH IT.
SHE'S AWAKE!
...?

WELCOME BACK.

CAKE

TO THE LIBERATORS!
TO THE LIBERATORS!
TO THE LIBERATORS!

EVERYONE HELPED. HERE'S TO EVERYONE.
BLUSH

SO, FOR TODAY, ENJOY BEING HEROES!
YOU TWO DID THE MOST.
HMM
OH, EMMET, HEY, MAN.

EMPHASIS IS ON "TODAY." WE DON'T LET ANYONE BE HEROES FOR MORE THAN A DAY. HERO WORSHIP TENDS TO CORRUPT. OR TURN YOU INTO AN ERLENMEYER.

UNDER-STOOD.

HOWEVER, FOR GOING ABOVE AND BEYOND THE CALL OF DUTY, YOU'RE PROMOTED TO OFFICIAL RESCUE MISSION DRIVER. WE STASHED THE VAN FOR LATER USE.

THAT DEATH TRAP?!

THAT *RESCUE VEHICLE.*

NO, YOU'RE NOT GOING ANY-WHERE WITH US. YOU'RE STILL A HATEFUL, TRAITOROUS, BLACK-HEARTED NAYSAYER.
NUH-UH!

I'VE CHANGED! I LIKE YOU GUYS NOW. I WANT TO GO WITH YOU.

YOU'RE SO FULL OF IT. YOU'RE STAYING RIGHT HERE.
NO
NO
NO
NO!

...
THERE'S...
THERE'S SOMETHING I WANT TO SAY TO YOU GUYS.

HE HAS TO GO WITH YOU. YOU BROUGHT HIM. HE'S YOUR RESPONSIBILITY. THE WEASEL *MUST* GO.
NOD
NOD

....?

I WANT TO APOLOGIZE.

AT THE TIME WE... *MET*, I FELT I WAS DOING THE RIGHT THING. BUT AFTER SEEING THE KIDS IN FREELAND, AND THE HOSPITAL WHERE YOU GUYS WERE, AND THE CURVE DOG...

...FINE.
FINE. WE'LL TAKE HIM ALONG.

SNF
UH.

SNF
SNF
...
...MAYBE PEOPLE REALLY CAN CHANGE.
HM.

HA HA HA HA

CLEAN CORN FOR CLEAN PEOPLE:
WE GUARANTEE THIS PRODUCT
HAS NOT BEEN SPRAYED, GENETI-
CALLY MODIFIED, OR TAMPERED
WITH BY SPELLCASTERS.
NEW ORDER.

RRUSTLE

Z
DID THIS REALLY USED TO BE OUR TOWN?

LOOK, THERE!
STOP
KTK

....!
THAT'S OUR TREE.
WHERE'S OUR HOUSE? WHERE'RE MOM AND DAD?
...SO THIS IS WHAT HOME LOOKS LIKE NOW. THE NEW ORDER WILL PAY FOR THIS.
...
HEY. REMEMBER THAT RHYME... THEY'D ALWAYS SAY IT WHEN WE CAME BACK HOME FROM A VACATION?
...YEAH. HOW DOES IT GO? NORTH...

...EAST, SOUTH, AND WEST, OUR HOME IS IN THE CENTER.
THOUGH WE MAY ROAM, OUR HOME IS BEST, AND SPEAK LOVE, YOU MAY ENTER.
THEY MADE US LEARN THAT, AND SAY IT WITH THEM.
...YEAH.
...!
AND SPEAK LOVE, YOU MAY ENTER.
SPEAK LOVE. SPEAK LOVE!
...

LOVE.
LOVE.
RRUSTLE

MOM! DAD!!
PASS
...!
...ARE YOU DEAD? ARE YOU HALF-LIGHTS?
WE'RE NOT DEAD, WISTY. WE'RE JUST SOMEWHERE ELSE. YOU'LL SEE THE REAL US SOON ENOUGH. I HOPE SO.
MAGIC HAS BROUGHT US TO YOU TODAY... SOMEONE ELSE'S MAGIC. WE JUST WANT TO TELL YOU...

...HOW PROUD WE ARE OF YOU.

YOUR TIME IN PRISON. HOW YOU RESCUED THE CHILDREN. HOW YOU DEALT WITH THAT EVIL AND UNWORTHY JUDGE. YOU'VE DONE AMAZINGLY WELL.

YOU TWO ARE THE PRESENT, AND THE FUTURE. AND NOW WE KNOW YOU CAN DO IT. THIS HAS JUST BEEN A WARM-UP.

NOD
DO YOU HAVE YOUR JOURNAL? AND YOU, WISTY, DO YOU HAVE YOUR DRUM-STICK?
OKAY, WISTY, YOU'RE READY TO DO THIS.
TRANSFORM THAT STICK INTO ITS TRUE FORM. DON'T BE AFRAID, JUST LOOK INTO MY EYES.

NOW, YOU DO IT, WHIT. OPEN THE JOURNAL AND LOOK AT ME.
.....!!
FLIP FLIP
FLIP
.....!!
THIS HAS EVERYTHING A WITCH AND WIZARD NEED TO KNOW.

WE ADORE YOU BOTH. BUT WE HAVE TO SAY GOOD-BYE FOR NOW.
WE LOVE YOU SO MUCH. GOOD-BYE. FOR A WHILE ANYWAY.
NO! STAY!
MOM! I LOVE YOU! COME BACK!
PLEASE DON'T LEAVE US ALREADY!

SNF
...

FLIP
FLIP

HEY, LOOK.
...?
"HOW TO DE-WEASEL SOMEONE: IF YOU'VE ACCIDENTALLY TURNED SOMEONE INTO A WEASEL..."

...

HAHAHA
SHRED THAT PAGE, PLEASE, WILL YOU?
YEAH, THAT'S RIGHT!
HEY, YOU NEVER KNOW. THE WEASEL MIGHT COME IN HANDY AS A HUMAN AT SOME POINT.

...
DON'T LOOK AT ME LIKE THAT. YOUR MOM DID IT. SHE SAID I SHOULD WATCH OVER YOU TWO.
SHRUG

OKAY, LET'S GO, WITCH. WE'VE GOT THINGS TO DO, KIDS TO SAVE, A NEW ORDER TO CRUSH.
SLAP
OKAY, WIZARD.
...IS ANYONE ELSE HUNGRY?

AND OFF WE WENT TO CRUSH THE NEW ORDER.

EXCEPT THINGS DIDN'T GO EXACTLY ACCORDING TO PLAN.

WHICH, OF COURSE, BRINGS US BACK TO WHERE WE BEGAN.

WAITING TO BE HUNG UNTIL DEAD, IN A STADIUM FILLED WITH CRAVEN LOOKY-LOOS...

...PRESIDED OVER BY A FIEND WHO SCARES THE SNOT OUT OF ME.

N

THE SCARIEST PART ISN'T THE OBVIOUS POWER HE'S GOT OVER THIS SLACK-JAWED CROWD, NO.
N.O.

THE THING THAT FREAKS ME OUT IS THAT I CAN TELL HE'S GOT MAGIC.
A LOT OF IT. SERIOUS MOJO.
N.

HOW OFTEN IN HUMAN HISTORY HAS SOMEBODY LIKE HIM TAKEN CONTROL OF A WHOLE SOCIETY?
N.O.
N.O.
YOU KNOW THE ANSWER, MY FRIENDS: FAR TOO OFTEN.
N.O.
SO HOW ARE YOU DOING— WHEREVER YOU ARE?

WE ALL KNOW FROM HISTORY WHAT CAN HAPPEN IF WE JUST STAY QUIET AND JUST DO WHAT'S PUT IN FRONT OF US.

AND DON'T WORRY TOO MUCH ABOUT WHIT AND ME.

WORD OF WHAT HAPPENS NEXT WILL GET TO YOU. I PROMISE.

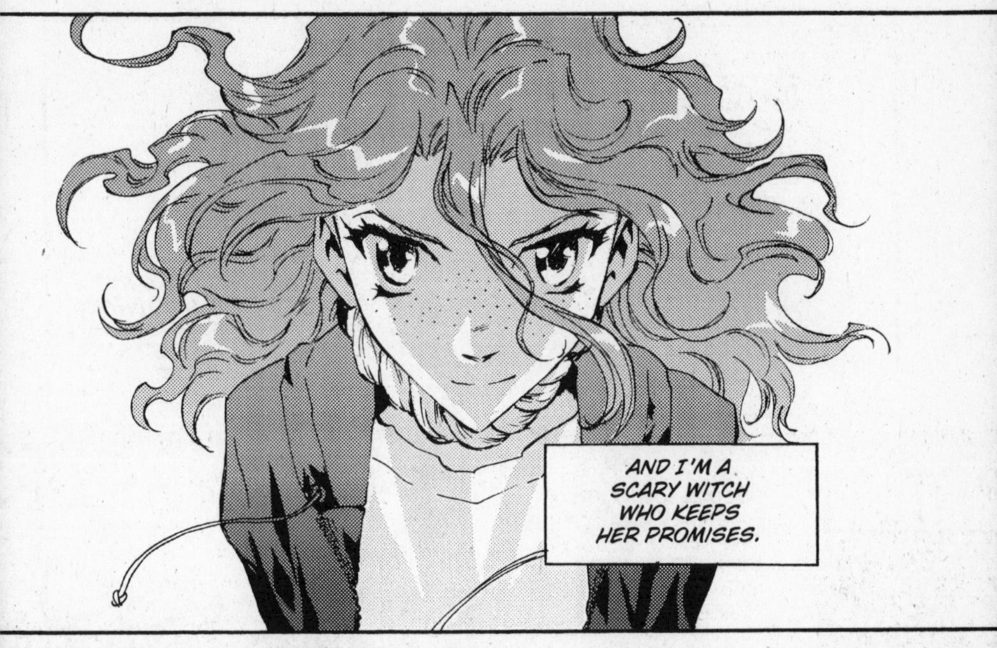
AND I'M A SCARY WITCH WHO KEEPS HER PROMISES.

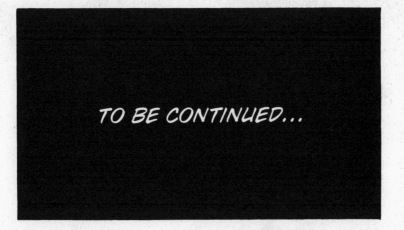

TO BE CONTINUED...

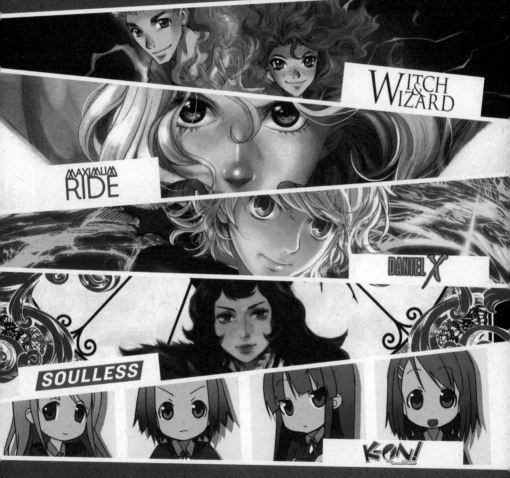

WITCH & WIZARD: THE MANGA ①

JAMES PATTERSON
WITH **GABRIELLE CHARBONNET**
& **SVETLANA CHMAKOVA**

Adaptation and Illustration: Svetlana Chmakova

Inking/toning assistant: Dennis Lo
Toning assistant: Eric Kim
Toning assistant: Sasha Chmakova
Lettering: JuYoun Lee

Yen Press
Hachette Book Group
237 Park Avenue, New York, NY 10017

www.HachetteBookGroup.com
www.YenPress.com

Yen Press is an imprint of Hachette Book Group, Inc. The Yen Press name and logo are trademarks of Hachette Book Group, Inc.

First Yen Press Edition: September 2011

ISBN: 978-0-316-11989-4

10 9 8 7 6 5 4 3 2 1

BVG

Printed in the United States of America